Fructus Humuli

Bulbus Allii sativi

Herba Plantaginis lanceolatae

THE DICTIONARY OF
HEALING PLANTS

THE DICTIONARY OF
HEALING PLANTS

Dr Hans-Peter Dörfler and Prof. Gerhard Roselt

Illustrated by
Ruth and Heinz Weber

BLANDFORD PRESS

LONDON · NEW YORK · SYDNEY

First published in the UK 1989 by Blandford Press,
an imprint of Cassell PLC
Artillery House, Artillery Row, London SW1P 1RT

Distributed in the United States by
Sterling Publishing Co., Inc.,
2 Park Avenue, New York, NY 10016

Distributed in Australia by
Capricorn Link (Australia) Pty Ltd
PO Box 665, Lane Cove, NSW 2066

British Library Cataloguing in Publication Data

Dorfler, Hans-Peter
  The Dictionary of healing plants
  1. Medical plants—Dictionaries
  I. Title II. Roselt., Gerhard III. Derrick
  Tony IV. Heilpflanzen. *English*
5816'34'0321   QK99.A1

ISBN 0 7137 1852 8

Typeset by Wordstream Ltd., Bournemouth, Dorset
Printed in The German Democratic Republic.

CONTENTS

Foreword

This book describes the most important healing plants native to Central Europe with comprehensive information about their medical significance. It will be found a great advantage when using the book that the text and plate for each plant appear on facing pages. The key diagnostic features of each plant have been accurately reproduced by the artists, so a more detailed botanical description is superfluous for our purposes. The most commonly found plants are described — even such despised and hated "weeds" as the plantain of our lawns and the stinging nettle, both of considerable medicinal worth. Details are given about their habitats and distribution, making them easier to find in the wild.

The guidance given about correct harvesting is essential if the valued medicinal constituents of plants are to be preserved intact. We also indicate the roles these plants have played in the past as well as the present, how they were originally used, and any side effects or poisoning users should be aware of. We strongly warn the adventurous against do-it-yourself treatment, since even the best knowledge of healing plants does not replace the trained herbalist.

We should also like to point out that important though it is to make the best possible use of these healing plants, it is vital to protect them from over-use and possible extinction. Existing laws protecting wild flowers should be respected and any drugs needed in quantity should either be raised by seed or bought from herbalists who cultivate them on a field scale.

Our special thanks go to the graphic artists, Ruth and Heinz Weber, who have helped us obtain plants or assisted us with key advice and literature.

Hants-Peter Dörfler
Gerhard Roselt

7

Introduction

Plants were man's first food and for long remained the most important. We can assume that prehistoric man had already learnt to distinguish edible plants from poisonous ones and in the course of time became acquainted with the supposedly magical powers of various plants to drive the demons of sickness out of their bodies – a superstitious belief that survived until the eighteenth century.

The first findings of drugs we still use today date back to the lake- dwelling era. The great importance of herbal medicines from the earliest times is evidence of an ancient tradition that goes back to the time of the Sumerians' cuneiform inscriptions, about 5000 BC. The Medes, Persians and Indians, and in the second century BC, the Chinese Emperor Shen Nung, all described healing plants. The 80 plants described in the Egyptian Ebers papyrus of the second century BC are clearly and factually set out according to their uses and dosage.

Over a thousand years later, Greek medicine led the field under Hippocrates. Aristoteles and particularly his disciple Theophrastus, the Father of Botany, studied healing plants. But Dioscorides was the first to produce a book on the subject, his *Great Pharmacology*, which detailed some 500 healing plants and remained valid for the next 15 centuries, dominating its field in the Middle Ages. Though it lacked illustrations, this was fully compensated for by its detailed and exact descriptions. Of equal importance were the works of Pliny, who passed on the collected scientific knowledge of ancient medicine.

Galen, who refused to believe that only drugs from Crete were effective and applied himself to ascertaining the exact dosages to be used, is considered to be the Father of Pharmacology. Even today preparations made without chemical reactions are referred to as Galenic medicines, a term that only came into use in the seventeenth century to distinguish such medicines from Paracelsus' remedies.

In Central Europe the Benedictines were particularly interested in the cultivation of healing plants, an activity encouraged by Charlemagne's Land Reform Act, *capitulare de villis*, in the year AD 800.

As the medicine-men had done earlier, those members of religious orders who were also active as doctors or apothecaries and recorded their knowledge, combined their successes in healing with the teaching of the church. It is plain from the following example of ergot of rye that despite some scientific knowledge poisonings occurred as well as practical successes.

Ergot of rye was long considered to be simply deformed grains of rye, which were ground along with the normal ones. A mere 1 per cent of such impurity can result in poisoning, yet in times of hardship the grain from which bread was made contained up to 30 per cent ergot. Monks and other religious followers were protected from poisoning by the purification of their grain, but the poor suffered severely. Either the nervous system was injured, with itching of the skin (itching sickness), long-lasting muscular spasms (cramp disease) and often attacks like epilepsy, or infection produced the burning disease ignis sacer (holy fire), with pains in the limbs, accompanied by a severe burning sensation. The limbs turned dark red, then black, and finally fell off from lack of blood.

When the sick took refuge in the cloisters, where they received a healing draught and clean bread, their condition quickly improved, but it deteriorated again after their release when they started eating contaminated bread once more. Although Johann Taube recognised that ergot of rye was the cause of ergotism as long ago as 1782, serious poisoning still occurred in Ireland in 1929 and in France in 1951.

Besides the Graeco-Roman influence, the Arabs' knowledge of healing plants flourished in the tenth century in the Moorish universities of Spain, where medical knowledge from the ancient world, Persia and India was combined and introduced to Central Europe.

While scholasticism had a great influence on medicine in the Middle Ages and established quotations were preferred to the results of experiments, a fundamental change took place in medical science with the transition to modern times.

Galen's anatomy, based on animal dissection, was replaced by Vesalius' *Textbook of Anatomy* (1542), with drawings based on the dissection of dead human bodies. The discovery of America and the sea routes to India brought a flood of new healing plants. The invention of the art of printing and the flowering of wood engraving led to the publication in quick succession of three important herbals, which show how much healing plants were valued. These were Brundfels, 1530; Fuchs, 1542; and Bock, 1546.

Valerius Cordus, publisher of the first German *Pharmacopoeia*, also lived at this time, as did Paracelsus, who introduced chemistry into medical science, yet delayed its development by reviving the teaching on signatures (*Signatura Plantarum*). Each plant was said to display an external sign indicating what it was effective for (e.g. thistles for shooting pains, red flowers for the blood, yellow flowers for the gall bladder, walnut for the brain.)

The importance of healing plants, the only organic medicine, apart from a few animal drugs, until the middle of the fifteenth century, continued to increase until that time. Then, following the isolation and synthesis of active substances from vegetable materials and doctors' demands for pure drugs that could be dispensed in accurate doses and whose effectiveness could easily be checked, herbs declined in importance for a while, becoming just raw materials for drugs. But with advances in analysis, new extraction and separation methods, and standardisation, a fresh impetus was given to research into healing plants.

Medicinal plants are a cheap source of raw materials. Their ingredients serve as model substances, their toxicity can be reduced by chemical action, and their effectiveness can be increased or given new characteristics. Since the human system has the necessary means to break them down, biogenic medicines are often more acceptable than synthetic products. The bulky materials cause a complex pharmacological action, which explains their superiority over pure products, as the unknown compounds they contain increase their effectiveness, influence their reabsorption or stabilise their ingredients.

The pharmacological testing of isolated substances has in most cases confirmed knowledge that has existed for thousands of years. But judgement becomes difficult when dealing with a particularly mild effect, or where the active substance has first to be determined. The supposed constituent may prove ineffective, while the total extract of the drugs is effective, as demonstrated by the pharmacology of valerian.

It is therefore increasingly necessary to test drugs by means of clinical pharmacology. While efforts are being made to optimise the cultivation of healing plants by selection, hybridisation and mutations, helped by genetics, one must remember that of the 600,000 plants on earth only 6 per cent have been tested pharmacologically, about 50 per cent of the medicines used today are based on biogenic materials and only 10 per cent are pure preparations from healing plants. On the other hand the extinction of a species that has not yet been used in this way cannot be reversed. Ethology is now being brought into play for this purpose. Various countries' traditional folk medicines are researched in an effort to find and test new medicinal substances.

The whole idea of folk medicine was long discounted as mere quackery. But the story of the plantain's wound-healing powers clearly indicates that many potential drugs are still unused. This plant was used worldwide for centuries for this purpose, yet only in the last few decades have any constituents with a worthwhile physiological effect been isolated.

Ribwort and greater plantain can be traced right back to the New Stone Age in Central Europe. They were mentioned by the Assyrians and by Dioscorides, though not by the followers of Hippocrates. They were also discovered independently by the Nordic peoples, and Leonhart Fuchs refers to ancient sources in his *New Herbal* of 1542, while at much the same time Hieronymus Bock (1546) praised the plantain as the most useful of all herbs.

Species of plantain were mentioned in the legends of the Nordic peoples as a treatment for wounds. The instruction repeatedly arises that "one side heals, but the other pulls" which is contradictory. But the smooth upper surface is usually said to be the part that heals.

The leaf was usually perforated, its ribs removed, then crushed before being applied to the wound. It is uncertain whether it was used to obtain a discharge of blood serum or by destroying the cell membrane to gain entry for the effective ingredients to the wound.

11

The fact that the North American Indians adopted the plantain, which was first brought to their country by the English and French, for healing wounds, and continued to use it for 200 years, indicates that something more than the traditional belief in its healing powers was involved. It is also remarkable that no case of tetanus has been known from using such a ground-hugging plant on open wounds.

Apart from its use on wounds and burns, this plant played its part worldwide in the first half of the twentieth century as a blistering agent for bites by rabid dogs and venemous snakes, for bee stings and for removing thorns and splinters. In earlier times it almost replaced antiseptics and was often used for ulcers.

Aucubin, isolated in 1907, is not the plantain's effective ingredient, but the aglycon aucubigenin, product of a hydrolytic splitting of beta-glucosidases, which was recognised in 1962. This substance is not an original content of the plant but can only be formed if the enzymes have not been destroyed by heating.

Healing plants with their manifold combinations of ingredients are therefore complex medicinal materials and each intervention in the specific reaction mechanism brings with it a flood of new problems, as can only happen with living material.

Authors' note

Throughout the text symbols
have been used to denote the following pieces of information:

* protected or rare plant
† poisonous plant

YARROW   *Achillea millefolium* L.

Family: Compositae (Asteraceae)

Description: The round roots creep underground and in spring produce leaf and flowering shoots up to 60 cm (24 in) tall. The leaves form basal rosettes on the leaf shoots. The numerous small flowers are grouped into inflorescences at the tops of the stems. Each flower has about five white, occasionally pink to carmine, peripheral ray florets. The type can be subdivided into several sub-species according to its location, differing from each other in appearance.

Flowering time: Summer to mid-autumn or fall.

Habitat: Yarrow is a herbaceous plant commonly found in dryish soil in the plains right up to the Alpine region. It is also found widely on roadsides, railway embankments and field boundaries.

Distribution: Yarrow can be found all over Europe right up to the north cape. Eastwards its habitat extends as far as the western Himalayas and Siberia. It was introduced by settlers into North America, South Australia and New Zealand in quite recent times.

Parts used: Herbage (Herba Millefolii).

Harvesting time: Summer to early autumn or fall.

Harvesting instructions: As flowering begins the top growth up to 20 cm (8 in) long is cut off and dried in a thin layer at temperatures below 30°C. The official drug comes from the cultivated sub-species *Achillea millefolium collina* and from material harvested in south-east and eastern Europe. Yarrow has a weak aromatic smell and a bitter-aromatic taste.

Ingredients: The drug contains ethereal oils (approximately 0.2 – 0.5 per cent) which contain various terpenes such as pines, sabinen, bornylacetate, camphor, artemisiaketon and cineol. The bitter tasting proazulene matricine is only contained in ethereal oils of sub-species of tetraploids which correspond to the above-mentioned sub-species. Other constituents are flavonoids and tannin agents.

Uses: Yarrow foliage is prescribed as an appetite-stimulating digestant, as a carminative and for its effects on the bile for gastro-intestinal complaints. These effects are attributed to its bitter principles, its ethereal oil, its tannins and flavonoids. Its blood-clotting and anti-inflammatory effect (resulting from its proazulene content) is used internally and externally. The drug is also used as a diuretic.

Side effects: Wet skin that has come into contact with this plant blisters on exposure to sunlight.

History: Achilles is said to have used this plant as a vulnerary. Dioscorides mentions it as the "soldier's herb". In the Middle Ages, it was valued above all as a coagulant.

Yarrow

† ACONITE (Common Monkshood)
Aconitum napellus L.

* **Family:** Ranunculaceae
Description: This is a herbaceous plant about ½ to 1½ m (½-1½ yds) high which survives the winter by means of its tuberous, turnip-like, thickened, fleshy root stock from which grow many branched fibrous roots. The digitate divided foliage is dark green above and light green beneath. Its dark violet flowers are arranged in many-flowered clusters, the blooms in the side clusters usually being somewhat smaller than those in the terminal clusters. The stalked flowers are covered with fine hair inside. Its numerous stamens enclose the three carpels, each of which has a follicle containing shiny black seeds.
Flowering time: Mid-summer to early autumn or fall.
Habitat: Aconite is found growing sporadically, or sometimes in large groups, and favours damp, humous-rich soil and well fertilised ground. It can be found beside paths, fences and watercourses, in thickets in pastures, around mountain huts and in mountain pastures.
Distribution: The plant is found in mountainous parts of Europe. Its habitat stretches as far north as Sweden. It is quite common in the Carpathian mountains and the Alps, where it grows at heights up to 3000 m (9800 ft).
Parts used: Tuberous root (Tubera Aconiti).
Harvesting time: Late summer to early autumn or fall.
Harvesting instructions: The harvested material is cleaned and if necessary broken up, then dried quickly at 40°C to prevent the aconitine being hydrolysed to the almost useless aconine. The drug is odourless and has a sweet, and later scratchy taste which causes a choking sensation.
Beware! Aconitine is one of the most poisonous alkaloids!
Ingredients: The tuberous roots contain 0.2−3 per cent alkaloids depending on the time of year and size. The main alkaloid is the unstable aconitin, secondary alkaloids are mesaconitine, hypaconitine, neopelline and napelline, alkamines, organic acids, sugar, fat.
Uses: Only plant preparations of exactly determined aconitine content, preferably aconitine nitrate, are used medically. It was first used for feverish colds but now is used more commonly both internally and externally for nerve pains, especially trigeminal neuralgia.
Toxic effect: About 2 g of the drug or 3 mg aconitine taken orally constitutes a fatal dose for adults. Poisoning is marked by excessive salivation, cramp, vomiting, difficulty in breathing, intestinal colic and heart or breathing failure. The main reason for poisoning is usually mistaking the roots for those of celery or horseradish.
History: Aconite has been recognised as a poisonous plant from the earliest times and was used as an arrow poison. Pliny described it as "vegetable arsenic". Aconitine was discovered in 1820.

16

Aconite

SWEET FLAG   *Acorus calamus* L.

Family: Araceae.

Description: Sweet flag survives the winter by means of its thumb-thick root stock (rhizome). The rhizome bears leaf scars on its upper surface, while underneath develop its sparsely-branched roots which anchor it firmly in the mud of the riverbank. The characteristic sweet flag smell comes from the rhizome. As with all Araceae the terminal inflorescence is 6–8 cm (2–3 in) long, and projects sideways from the main stem with many small yellowish green to light brown hermaphrodite flowers covering its spadix. The fruit is a reddish berry which does not develop in temperate climates, however. In Europe it increases exclusively by means of the 20 cm (8 in) or more annual growth of its rhizome.

Flowering time: Early to mid-summer.

Habitat: Sweet flag can be found on the banks of still or flowing water and sometimes also in marshy places but never where it dries out.

Distribution: Sweet flag is found throughout Central and Eastern Europe and the Balkans, as well as tropical and sub-tropical East Asia and Eastern Siberia. It can also be found in North America. The plant was introduced into Europe at the end of the sixteenth century.

Parts used: Rootstock. (Rhizoma Calami).

Harvesting time: Early to mid-autumn or fall.

Harvesting instructions: The rootstocks (rhizomes) are dug out, washed and freed from secondary roots, broken up and dried. The drug has a strong aromatic smell and a spicy and bitter taste and comes from both locally harvested and imported material.

Ingredients: Rhizoma calami contains 1.5–3.5 per cent essential oils in a changing composition whose typical content is asaran, bitter constituents like acorone, asarone, and also tannin, mucin and starch.

Uses: The drug is prescribed for stomach and intestinal complaints. It stimulates the appetite, strengthens the stomach and helps the digestion so it is used as a strengthening and restorative medicine. It is also used for treating kidney stones and gall-bladder complaints. Drug extracts are used externally as a gargle and for gum diseases. Oleum calami is addéd to skin treatment baths, as well as to linaments for gout and rheumatism. Asaron is said to have a calming effect. A mixture of sweet flag powder and ammonium carbonate drives away ants.

Side effects: The drug is mild and harmless in therapeutic quantities.

History: The drug, which was used by the Greeks, probably originated in India. The followers of Hippocrates only used it externally; but it was always used as a spice.

Sweet Flag

†SPRING PHEASANT'S EYE *Adonis Vernalis* L.

*Family: Ranunculaceae.

Description: The 10−40 cm (4−15 in) high plant grows from a strong black-brown rootstock which develops simple and branched flowering and non-flowering shoots in the spring. Each branch of the fertile shoots ends in a large, radial, short-stemmed brilliant yellow flower, up to 7 cm (3 in) across when open. The flowers secrete no nectar so pollination is carried out only by pollen-collecting bees and pollinating beetles.

Flowering time: Mid to late spring.

Habitat: The plant is widely scattered in dry sunny ground in chalky or gypsum soil on lightly shaded hillsides, more rarely on sandy soil. It prefers steppe-like places, dry or dryish grassland, open oak and pine woods.

Distribution: The spring pheasant's eye's habitat is centred in the steppe-heathland of South-Eastern Europe. From there the species spread into Central Europe, particularly the Thuringian dry basin.

Parts used: Herbage (Herba Adonidis vernalis).

Harvesting time: Mid to late spring.

Harvesting instructions: The herbage must be delivered in as fresh a condition as possible as only properly dried drugs keep their active properties for a long time. Heating it for 30 minutes to 60°C stabilises the glycoside valued for heart treatment. After this it is dried at 30°C. Spring pheasant's eye herbage is odourless but has an aromatic bitter taste.

Beware! Spring pheasant's eye herbage is poisonous!

Ingredients: The drug contains approximately 1 per cent of the digitalis-like effective glycoside, adonidosid, adonivernosid, cymarine and adonitoxin. Other constituents are the flavonoids, adonite and choline.

Uses: Standard drug extracts from fresh plants are used, as the glycosides, similar in structure to the foxglove's, are very sensitive. Like digitalis glycosides they have an exceptional effect on a damaged heart but as they are not cumulative they can be prescribed over a longer period as part of the medical treatment of heart and circulatory complaints.

Toxic effect: Side effects can occur, such as irritation of the gastrointestinal tract. An overdose can cause sickness, vomiting, stomachache and diarrhoea, but no fatal poisoning.

History: Hippocrates used spring pheasant's eye herbage. It was later used for kidney stones, urinary troubles and dropsy.

Spring Pheasant's Eye

HORSE CHESTNUT *Aesculus hippocastanum* L.

Family: Hippocastanaceae.

Description: The horse chestnut, which can reach a height of 35 m (115 ft), is a stately tree with an arched crown and, when mature, pendulous branches. Its thick trunk is anchored in the ground by many strong, horizontal roots. The thick sticky buds are already obvious in autumn, then in spring develop into the 20 cm (8 in) long finger-shaped leaves. The candle-shaped inflorescences bear many flowers whose white petals are tinted yellow, later reddish, at the base. The fine velvety ovary develops into a prickly green spherical capsule which contains the familiar shiny brown seed with the light hilum mark.

Flowering time: Late spring to early summer.

Habitat: The horse chestnut is a tree of deep humus-rich soil and is often planted as an ornamental tree.

Distribution: The horse chestnut came originally from the gorges of the northern Balkan Peninsula and the Western Caucasus. Having been cultivated since the sixteenth century throughout Europe apart from its northern-most areas.

Parts used: Seeds (Semen Hippocastani).

Harvesting time: Early to mid autumn or fall.

Harvesting instructions: The ripe seeds are harvested and must then be delivered for further processing immediately, as they are easily attacked by mould.

Ingredients: The seed contains a mixture of saponins, one of is described as aescine which easily crystalises, as well as flavonoid glycosides, albumin and fatty oils.

Uses: The plant contains aescine which is used medically and extracts from the seeds are used industrially, especially for complaints of the veins, such as phlebitis, haemorrhoids, varicose veins and their ulcers, to prevent thrombosis, for disturbed peripheral circulation, some cases of migraine, stroke oedemas and effusions of blood, for limb complaints and frostbite. The hydroxycumarin-glycoside aesculin from the bark of the branch absorbs ultra-violet rays and is an ingredient for suntan oil.

Side effects: Industrially produced horse chestnut preparations rarely have any side effects, even after months' long application. Any stomach upset that might occur disappears immediately one stops taking the preparation. Children who eat the seeds can suffer from saponine poisoning with fatal consequences.

History: While the bark was first listed in the Württemberg Pharmacopoeia in 1760, the seed was not chemically examined until the second half of the nineteenth century and used only for a few decades.

Horse Chestnut

AGRIMONY

Agrimonia eupatoria L.

Family: Rosaceae.
Description: Agrimony is a short-lived herbaceous perennial 30–60 cm (12–24 in) high with a creeping rootstock. In spring it generally develops a single upright stem with a few weak branches or none at all. The leaves at the base of the stem are dense and arranged like a rosette. The dark green upper surface of the leaves is covered in short velvety hairs. The light green underside of the leaves and the leaf stalks bear tufts of hairs. The small golden-yellow flowers are borne in a spike at the apex of the stem. Of the two carpels only one develops into a single-seeded achene, which remains locked into the calyx of the perigynous flower with hooked spines until it germinates.
Flowering time: Summer.
Habitat: The plant can be found in almost any soil but especially on loam. It prefers to colonise light dry woods, alongside fences and paths, and meadows and pastures.
Distribution: Because of its excellent seed-distribution system agrimony can be classed as almost universal in habitat.
Parts used: Herbage (Herba Agrimoniae).
Harvesting time: Summer.
Harvesting instructions: The herbage is cut off 1 cm above the ground before the plant has developed seeds and dried in thin layers. When harvesting it, be sure not to confuse it with black mullein (*Verbascum nigrum*). The drug has a distinct spicy smell and a harsh and bitter taste.
Ingredients: Agrimony herbage contains approximately 10 per cent tannin, bitter constituents and some ethereal oil, nicotinic acid amide, silicic acid, iron, vitamins B and K.
Uses: Nowadays the plant is rarely used as a tannin drug. It used to be prescribed for stomach upsets, digestive difficulties and gall-bladder troubles and externally for inflammations in the mouth, as a gargle for singers and speakers and as compresses for wounds and ulcers. The alcoholic extract of the drug is said to check the spread of viruses.
Side effects: No side effects are known.
History: Agrimony is an old healing plant which was mentioned by Dioscorides and Pliny. The plant, which was often described in the Middle Ages, is also used in folk medicine for diarrhoea, bedwetting, liver complaints, rheumatism and lumbago.

Agrimony

COUCH-GRASS

Agropyron repens L.
PAL.BEAUV.

Family: Gramineae (Poaceae).
Description: This perennial grass sends out far-reaching, white stolons underground and can grow 20 to 120 cm (8−47 in) tall. The leaf blades, typical of all grasses, are smooth and only hairy when young, the leaves are about 5 mm wide and mostly slightly involuted. The slender, roughly 10 cm (4 in) long flower spike stands erect with sometimes tightly, sometimes loosely packed spikelets, each with four to eight flowers. The hull and outer glumes both bear awns.
Flowering time: Early summer, sporadically to mid-autumn or fall.
Habitat: Couch-grass is mostly found on refuse heaps and waste-land, beside footpaths and in hedges. In fields and gardens it is known to us as a weed, difficult to eradicate. It grows on all kinds of soil from the lowlands to the mountains up to the 2100 m (6900 ft) levels.
Distribution: This plant is widespread in Europe, Siberia, North Africa and North America.
Parts used: Stolons (Rhizoma Graminis).
Harvesting time: Early to mid-spring and early to mid-autumn or fall.
Harvesting instructions: The stolons are washed, the secondary roots and glumes removed, then they are dried in thin layers. Their golden-yellow colour should then be preserved. The drug is odourless and has a sweet taste.
Ingredients: Couch grass roots contain 3−18 per cent triticine − a soluble polysaccharid, 3 per cent fructose, some mucilage and small quantities of saponins and ethereal oil, antibiotic substance, silicic acid, potassium, inosite.
Uses: The saponin content of the drug gives it a diuretic effect so it is an ingredient of bladder and kidney decoctions. It is less important as a mucus membrane covering agent and a mild laxative. The infusion as well as the freshly pressed juice, which was used in folk medicine, or the syrup produced by boiling, acts as a tonic due to its rich content of easily digestible carbohydrates.
Side effects: No side effects are known.
History: It is not certain which plant of the grass family was referred to in antiquity as a diuretic. In the Middle Ages couch-grass was often prescribed as a drug. Couch-grass was listed as Radix Graminis in Hamburg and Frankfurt in the sixteenth century.

Couch-grass

HOLLYHOCK

Althaea rosea L.

Family: Malvaceae.

Description: The hollyhock grows 1−3 m (3−10 ft) high and is usually biennial. The stiff upright stems carry alternate long-stemmed woolly haired leaves. The large 6−10 cm (2−4 in) wide flowers are borne on the upper part of the stem singly or in twos or fours in the axils of the leaves, which get smaller towards the apex. The lower flowers are stalked, the upper ones sessile, forming a long spike. The five petals can vary in colour e.g white, yellow, carmine or black-purple. The hypogynous ovary develops into a ring-shaped fruit which breaks up into numerous disc-like partial fruits. This plant is distinguished from the mallow (genus Malva) by its six to nine leaved outer calyx.

Flowering time: Mid-summer to early autumn or fall.

Habitat: The hollyhock can be found growing wild on railway embankments and riversides, on waste ground and near fences. It has been grown as an ornamental plant in Central Europe since the sixteenth century.

Distribution: The hollyhock probably originated in the Eastern Mediterranean region and was brought to Europe by the Turks or the Crusaders.

Parts used: Flowers (Flores Malvae arboreae)

Harvesting time: Mid-summer to early autumn or fall.

Harvesting instructions: When the flowers of the darker types have opened the calyx is carefully separated from the stem and dried in well ventilated conditions (preferably in a current of warm air). After drying they are nearly black. The drug is odourless and has a slimy, weak astringent taste and colours the saliva blue. It must be stored to protect it from damp in airtight containers.

Ingredients: The main constituents of Flores Malvae arboreae are mucilage, tannin and anthocyan-colouring.

Uses: The drug can be used as a mucilage for coughs and inflammatory illnesses of the respiratory organs and for stomach and intestinal catarrh. The hollyhock flowers without their calyces are of greater importance for colouring foods, particularly teas and wines. The plant is specially cultivated for this purpose in wine-growing areas.

Side effects: The drug is classed as harmless.

History: It is not certain whether the drug was known as a medicine in antiquity. It was first described in the fifteenth century, when its healing powers were also mentioned. It is possible, however, that the holyhock was already cultivated as a healing plant in Carolingian times.

Hollyhock

LADY'S-MANTLE   *Alchemilla vulgaris* L.

Family: Rosaceae.

Description: The height of this plant depends on its location. Sometimes it reaches only a few centimetres but it can be over 30 cm (12 in). Lady's-mantle survives by means of its oblique resting root which becomes very woody and gradually dies off at one end while the other continues to grow. The leaves, which are smooth or tufted with hair, are also folded when fully grown, with five to nine lobes and notched at the margins. The leaves of the inflorescence are only slightly incised in a star shape. The many-flowered inflorescence is smooth or has scattered hairs. The campanulate calyx has four calyx teeth, the same length as the receptacle of the perigynous flower.

Flowering time: Late spring to early autumn or fall.

Habitat: This widely distributed plant is found from the lowlands to the alpine regions. Most is in wet, fat meadows and pastures, waste ground and fields, in light woods and thickets.

Distribution: Lady's-mantle grows in most of Europe and Eastern North America and Greenland, and in Asia from the Caucasus and Himalayas to Siberia.

Parts used: Herbage (Herba Alchemillae).

Harvesting time: Late spring to late summer.

Harvesting instructions: After the dew has been dried off the leaves and stems are collected and dried in thin layers preserving the colour of the parts to be used. The drug is odourless and has a bitter astringent taste.

Ingredients: Herba Alchemillae contains tannin glycoside and traces of salicylic acid.

Uses: The drug is now used only rarely for stomach and intestinal complaints, especially for diarrhoea and flatulence, by reason of its tannin content. It is only occasionally used externally for badly healing wounds or as a bath additive.

Side effects: The plant has no known side effects.

History: Lady's-mantle was used as a drug in antiquity, because of the distinctive way dew forms on its leaves. Miraculous properties were attributed to the plant.

Lady's-Mantle

GARLIC

Allium sativum L.

Family: Liliaceae.

Description: The relatively small main bulb from which the flower stem arises, is surrounded by a number of daughter bulbs (cloves) of similar size, together covered in a white skin-like sac, forming an almost fist-sized, globular compound bulb, slightly depressed at the base. The flower stem grows up to 1 m (3 ft) high with leaves on its lower half. The few-flowered umbel is surrounded by a very long beaked tunic which opens during flowering and later falls off. A few long-stemmed flowers grow between stem bulbils up to 1 cm across.

Flowering time: Mid to late summer.

Habitat: The plant is widely grown in vegetable gardens and occasionally as a farm crop.

Distribution: As with many old cultivated plants its original homeland is uncertain. Garlic grows wild in the East, in Central Asia and in the East Indies and is also cultivated there, so it probably originated there.

Parts used: Bulb (Bulbus Allii sativi).

Harvesting time: Early to mid-autumn or fall.

Harvesting instructions: When the plants' leaves have died off the bulbs are harvested and dried in bundles. The drug has a characteristic sharp smell and a sharp biting, spicy taste.

Ingredients: The drug contains various vitamins and supplies approximately 0.2 per cent ethereal oil which has an unpleasant smell. Essential oil contains sulphur, diallyldisulphide, allicin, alliin, trace of selenium, vitamins A and C with nicotinic acid. When grinding down the fresh bulbs the odourless, antibiotic, ineffective alliin is changed by the enzyme alliinase into the antibiotic, effective allicin.

Uses: Fresh bulbs are used, or alcoholic extracts whose alliinase has been destroyed, so that the preparation is odourless. It has been shown that, apart from the antibiotic effect of the allicin, there is a beneficial effect on arteriosclerosis and high blood pressure, attributed to the alliin. Garlic has an appetising and carminative effect and promotes digestion. It is prescribed for infectious illnesses of the intestinal system and is said to be effective against worms.

Side effects: Poisoning from the plant is unlikely. The oil is only slightly poisonous but can, however, cause severe inflammation and damage the kidneys if given in large doses or over a long period.

History: As both seasoning and medicine garlic can be traced back via Rome, Athens and Egypt to the ancient Indian civilisation. Garlic was the main food of the poor in ancient times.

Garlic

MARSH MALLOW   *Althaea officinalis* L.

Family: Malvaceae.

Description: This herbaceous perennial grows from 60 to 150 cm (2−5 ft) high and is covered throughout in velvety hair. To start with it grows a spindle-like root, but this is soon replaced by a horizontal, creeping, finger-thick, branched rootstock. Usually several upright, simple or little-branched stems arise from a single root. The lower leaves are cordate and pointed, but those right at the top are often undivided. The beautiful, light pink, rarely whitish, flowers are carried in clusters, each of a few blooms, in the leaf axils or at the apex of the stem.

Flowering time: Mid-summer to early autumn or fall.

Habitat: Marsh mallow mainly colonises salty or potash-rich soil, in which it probably originated. But scattered plants are also found in damp meadows, riverside thickets, and pastures, and it is also grown agriculturally.

Distribution: This plant grows only in Atlantic Europe. In the North it grows up as far as Southern Scandinavia, and also in the areas around the Eastern Mediterranean, Black Sea and Caspian Sea and further east to the Altai and Siberia.

Parts used: Root (Radix Althaeae), leaves (Folia Althaeae).

Harvesting time: Root, mid to late autumn or fall, leaves, late spring to early summer.

Harvesting instructions: The root is mainly used, being split and dried as quickly as possible at 60°C to avoid a mildew attack. The leaves have to be watched while being dried for any developing rust fungus. The marsh mallow root has a weak but distinctive smell but the leaves are odourless. Both drugs are slimy.

Ingredients: The main and most important ingredient of the roots and leaves of the marsh mallow is mucilage, with traces of essential oil.

Uses: Because of its mucilage content it is used as a cold water extraction, syrup or tea ingredient, as a soothing, cough relieving medicine and analgesic for throat and chest complaints. Marsh mallow also has a beneficial effect on the digestive system and is added to locally irritating medicines.

Side effects: Marsh mallow is a mild product and is often used in the treatment of children.

History: The healing properties of this plant were known to the Greeks and Romans. Dioscorides, Theophrastus, Galen and Pliny mention the drug in their writings. Charlemagne encouraged the cultivation in peasants' gardens. It was in general use in the Middle Ages.

Marsh Mallow

DILL
(Peucedanum graveolens)

Anethum graveolens L.

Family: Umbelliferae.

Description: Dill is a single-stemmed annual plant about 40–125 cm (15–49 in) high and fragrant, especially when ground down. The upright, tubular stem is finely grooved and marked with alternate white and green longitudinal stripes. It is covered with leaves which are mostly bi- or tri-, rarely quadripinnate. The small flowers are gathered in umbels, which in the cultivated form are larger with more rays reaching 15 cm (6in) across. When ripe the dehiscent fruit interwoven with oil channels easily separates into two lentil-shaped partial fruits drawn out into a straw-yellow winged margin at the edges.

Flowering time: Mid-summer to early autumn or fall.

Habitat: Dill is a popular kitchen herb cultivated in gardens and fields. It can be found growing wild on pathways and cultivated land.

Distribution: Its home is probably in Iran, Eastern Indies, the Caucasus and Egypt. It occurs as a weed of cultivated land throughout the Mediterranean area, in Ethiopia and South Africa. It can also be found cultivated or wild in most parts of Europe, and in North, Central and South America.

Parts used: Fruits (Fructus Anethi).

Harvesting time: Mid-summer to early autumn or fall.

Harvesting instructions: The umbels are cut off and dried shortly before they ripen. The fruits then ripen and can easily be stripped. They have a pleasant strong spicy smell and taste sweet and burning at first but later spicy.

Ingredients: The dill fruits contain mainly ethereal oils (approximately 3–4 per cent) whose main constituent is carvone (terpene ketone $C_3 H_5 C_6 H_6O CH_3$).

Uses: Dill is hardly ever used nowadays as a laxative, appetiser and eupeptic or as a diuretic and carminative. Oleum anethi is said to have antibacterial and fungicidal properties. The fruit is used as a spice in herb meals and salads and when pickling gherkins.

Side effects: The drug is said to promote milk secretion and have a calming effect on insomnia.

History: The Egyptians, Greeks and Romans used this plant as a medicine and spice. It is assumed that Benedictine monks naturalised dill in Central Europe. The Carolingians cultivated it in their palace gardens.

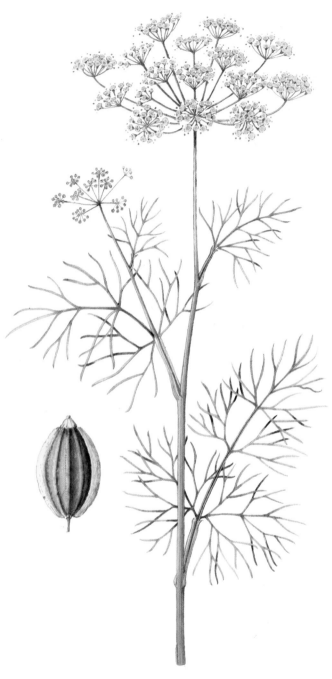

Dill

GARDEN ANGELICA   *Angelica archangelica* L.

Family: Umbelliferae.
Description: This generally biennial plant (rarely lasting up to four years) has a turnip-like root in its first year. In the second year a spongy rootstock about 5 cm (2 in) thick develops from this, which is covered in part with twisted roots and with a yellowish milky sap inside. The root, indeed the whole plant, has a strong spicy smell. Its one or two upright pithy tubular stems rarely reaching 3 m (10 ft) high are finely grooved, red-brown and branched at the top. The lower stem is set with 60−90 cm (2−3 ft) large, tripinnate foliage which decreases in size up the stem. The greenish to yellow flowers are arranged in large, hemispherical umbels on long stems. The base of the stem of the garden angelica and wild angelica (A. sylvestris) is round, that of the marsh angelica (A. palustris) has sharp-edged grooves. Garden angelica has greenish petals while those of wild angelica are white or reddish after full flowering.
Flowering time: Summer.
Habitat: Angelica grows sporadically in damp meadows and bogland, beside ditches and riverbanks and in thickets and alder woods. It is also cultivated on farms.
Distribution: The plant can be found in Northern Europe as far as Greenland, Iceland and the Faroe Islands. In the East it reaches the Altai mountains and Lake Baikal and in the south to Transylvania.
Parts used: Taproot (Radix Angelicae).
Harvesting time: Mid-autumn or fall.
Harvesting instructions: The rootstock and roots of biennial plants are dug out, washed, split longitudinally and dried at 40°C in a good current of air. The drug, all of it from cultivated plants, has a strong spicy smell and tastes at first sweet, then burning with a spicy-bitter taste.
Ingredients: The angelica root contains 0.3−0.5 per cent essential oil with phellandrene, angelica acid, bitters, cumarin compounds and tannin.
Uses: The use of this drug is limited to its effectiveness as a stomachic and its carminative qualities. The bitter ingredients and ethereal oil are the source of its appetising and digestion-promoting properties which stimulate the secretion of stomach acids and pepsin. Radix Angelicae is added to stomach and bitter liqueurs and also to baths.
Side effects: The juice of the fresh plant can produce so-called bathing dermatitis with blisters forming. Poisoning from garden angelica is unheard of though this could happen if it were misused.
History: Being a northern plant it was unknown to medicine in antiquity but it has been cultivated in Central Europe since the fourteenth century. Paracelsus praised its juice as the "best medicine" against internal infections.

Garden Angelica

COMMON CHAMOMILE   *Anthemis nobilis* L.

Family: Compositae (Asteraceae).
Description: The 15−30 cm (6−12 in) high plant survives by means of its deep-seated root. This produces several ascending, sometimes erect, simple or branched stems. The double pinnatifid, 2−4 cm (½−1½ in) long foliage may be covered in fluffy hairs or almost entirely bare. The flowers are arranged in small terminal stemmed flower heads, similar to those of the wild chamomile. The flower head is surrounded with long oval encasing scales. The whole base of the flower is extended and tapered. The 12 to 18 white, fertile ray florets are longer than the disc florets.
Flowering time: Early summer to early autumn or fall.
Habitat: Common chamomile's homeland is Southern Europe and it can be found in the Mediterranean area from Portugal to Iran.
Distribution: Common chamomile grows in Southern Europe on gravelly pastures, beside still waters and partly in dry locations. In Central Europe, where it has been grown since the sixteenth century, it grows particularly in farm gardens, usually in the double-flowered form, but is sometimes found growing wild.
Parts used: Flowers (Flores Chamomillae romanae).
Harvesting time: Early to mid-summer.
Harvesting instructions: Shortly before they are in full bloom the flowers of the so-called double variety, with flower heads most of whose tubular flowers have changed into ray florets, are collected and dried at 35°C. They have a strong aromatic smell and a spicy, bitter taste.
Ingredients: The drug contains up to 2.4 per cent ethereal oil with chamazulen, flavonoids, bitter constituents, sugar and resin.
Uses: Common chamomile, whose healing properties are those of wild chamomile, is seldom used nowadays. The drug is used internally for complaints of the intestinal tract and as an antispasmodic and externally for its anti-inflammatory effect on skin inflammations, wounds and burns. The flowers are used in hairdressing, e.g. to lighten darkened blonde hair. It was often used in the first half of this century in the treatment of menstruation problems (emmenagogue).
Side effects: Common chamomile has no side effects worth mentioning.
History: The drug has been used as a medicine since the sixteenth century. The ethereal oil derived by steam distillation of the dried flowers was entered in the Medical Appraisal of Frankfurt in 1587.

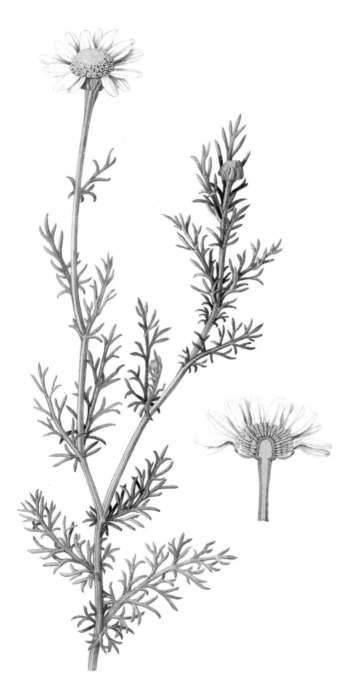

Common Chamomile

BURDOCK

Arctium spec.

Family: Compositae.
Description: This rough scaly plant up to 11/2 m (5 ft) tall has a fleshy spindle-shaped root, whitish within. The strong stem is well branched. The alternate entire foliage is petiolated. The slightly flattened spherical flower heads are attached to the main stem by long pedicels and arranged in clusters on the branches. The small involucral scales are bent inwards at the end and loosely linked by a cobweb-like layer. There are four types of burdock in Europe. The small flower heads of the felted burr (A. tomentosum MILL.) have straight blunt involucral scales generally with reddish tips; the other three species differ by having involucral scales with curved hooked tips. Burdock (A. lappa L.), also used medicinally, can be distinguished from the grove burr (A. nemorosum LEJ.) and small burr (A. minus) by its flower heads, which generally have green involucral scales and are arranged in loose clusters at the top. It grows taller (up to 3 m (10 ft) and has larger flower heads.
Flowering time: Mid-summer to early autumn or fall.
Habitat: These humus-loving plants can generally be found in colonies in the plains up to the mountain slopes, and also on footpaths, embankments, on waste ground and village greens.
Distribution: The small and great burr can be found in Europe northwards as far as Central Scandinavia. They are absent from the south but eastwards reach the Caucasus, the great burr as far as Japan.
Parts used: Root (Radix Bardanae).
Harvesting time: Early mid-spring and early to mid-autumn or fall.
Harvesting instructions: The roots of biennial plants are dried and stored in airtight tins to protect them from insect attack. The drug Radix Bardanae contains the roots of Arctium lappa, A. minus and A. tomentosum. It is odourless with a sweet slimy taste.
Ingredients: The various types of burr differ from each other mainly by their inulin content: A. lappa contains up to 45 per cent, A. minus up to 27 per cent and A. tomentosum up to 19 per cent inulin. Other ingredients are ethereal oil, tannin, mucilage and resin, with acids and antibiotic substance.
Uses: These plants are no longer used in medicine. In the past the drug was prescribed for stomach upsets of various kinds, as a diuretic and diaphoretic, and externally for skin complaints. It is now used as 'burdock oil' to promote the growth of hair.
Side effects: No side effects are known.
History: Galen mentions several types of burdock in his writings. The drug was also prescribed in the Middle Ages.

Burdock

BEARBERRY

Arctostaphylos uva-ursi
(L.) SPR.

Family: Ericaceae

Description: The bearberry is a dwarf evergreen shrub with wide-spreading branches, with dense-leaved upward-arching twigs which can form a carpet up to 10 cm (4 in) high. The whitish green, often pink-bordered, bell flowers are five-toothed. They are arranged in upright or slightly drooping clusters. The round mealy fruit is a scarlet red berry enclosed by a calyx at the base.

Flowering time: Mid-spring to early summer.

Habitat: The bearberry likes to grow in light, dry pinewoods and is often found as an interwoven carpet in the undergrowth. It can be found in flat country, particularly on heathland, and in high or fairly high mountains in both chalky and acid soils.

Distribution: The bearberry is a sub-arctic plant which occurs beyond the Urals and into Northern Siberia. In Southern Europe and Southern Asia, it is found only in high mountains and further afield in the northern parts of North America and Greenland.

Parts used: Leaves (Folia Uvae Ursi).

Harvesting time: Mid-spring to mid-summer.

Harvesting instructions: The small leaves are carefully plucked from the plants and dried in thin layers. The drug is odourless and has a bitter, astringent taste at first which later turns sweet.

Ingredients: Bearberry leaves contain mainly the glycosides arbutin and methylarbutin, the contents of which depend on the location of the plant and the time of year and vary between 5 and 11 per cent; furthermore they contain a high tannin content, flavonoids and resins.

Uses: The drug was prescribed as a cold water extract containing mainly glycosides and to a lesser extent tannin, for inflammation of the urinary system. In alkaline urine the glycosides are split, forming hydrochinon or methylhydrochinon, which has a bactericidal effect. After using bearberry leaves the urine colours olive-green to brown. The plant was also used for urinary calculus and bed wetting.

Side effects: Stomach upsets are possible when the drug is used for long periods due to its tannin content. Fatal hydrochinon poisoning is impossible when normal doses of the plant are given as a medicine.

History: The bearberry was first listed in an English pharmacopoeia in the twelfth century. But it was only in general use in the eighteenth century.

Bearberry

*ARNICA   *Arnica montana* L.

Family: Compositae
Description: This 20−60 cm (8−24 in) plant overwinters by means of its short, thick subterranean rootstocks. In spring it forms a rosette of oval leaves that lie flat on the ground. From the middle of this rosette rises a leafy stem with usually one, but occasionally two or more shiny egg-yellow flowers. These are formed by hermaphrodite disc florets and ligulate female ray florets which could however curl up or be missing. The whole plant has a strong aromatic smell.
Flowering time: Late spring to late summer.
Habitat: Arnica grows on humus-containing to sandy, infertile ground, from flat country right up to the high alpine slopes (over 2000 m (6,500 ft)) and hates lime. It grows on grassland, pastures, heaths, dried-out high bogland and light coniferous woodland.
Distribution: Arnica is a characteristic Central European mountain plant. It shuns dry areas so it is missing from the Pannonian Basic (Hungary) and the Mediterranean. It grows throughout Europe apart from Great Britain.
Parts used: Flowers (Flores Arnicae).
Harvesting time: Mid to late summer.
Harvesting instructions: The flowers of *Arnica montana* L. and *A. chamissonis* LESS., the meadow arnica, which is cultivated in Germany, are collected before they wilt and dried at 40-45°C. Flowers which have been attacked by insects are usually curled up and must be discarded. The drug has a spicy aromatic smell and a bitter scratchy taste.
Ingredients: Both plants contain up to 0.1 per cent ethereal oil, and other flavonoids, carotinoids and cholin, acetylene compounds and tannin.
Uses: Arnica is used externally as a dilute tincture for its anti-inflammatory and healing properties as well as its vasodilatory characteristics for wounds, effusions of blood, bruising, sprains, phlebitis and oedema. It is also effective against neuralgia, pains in the joints, boils and inflamed insect bites.
Side effects: The external use of a tincture which has not been diluted sufficiently can cause inflammation of the skin with the formation of blisters. Be warned against overdoses when using it as tea, for heart and circulatory complaints, for example.
History: The German tribes used arnica medicinally. After initial reluctance it became one of the most used medicines in the eighteenth century and has been the subject of chemical research since 1819.

Arnica

WORMWOOD   *Artemisia absinthium* L.

Family: Compositae.
Description: Wormwood is a 1 m (3 ft), sometimes 1½ m (5 ft) high sub-shrub whose rootstock usually survives from 3 to 10 years. Its high leaf rosettes and upright branches become woody and can survive the winter given favourable weather. The round, slightly grooved stems are paniculate and generously leafed. These appear silver-grey due to the tightly adpressed hair. There are many broadly globose flowers in each upright, many flowered panicle. All the yellow flowers are fertile, the disc florets hermaphrodite and the ray florets female. The plant has a strong aromatic smell and a bitter taste.
Flowering time: Mid summer to early autumn or fall.
Habitat: This plant prefers dry, chalky and fertile soil from the plains to the avalanche channels of the Central Alps. It can be found on waste ground, walls and pastures, rocky fields on the slopes and in arid regions.
Distribution: This species originated in the more or less salty steppes of Eastern Europe and Central Asia, but by its cultivation was widely dispersed and imported into many areas.
Parts used: Herbage while in flower (Herba Absinthii).
Harvesting time: Mid to late summer.
Harvesting instructions: The flowering herb is collected minus its woody stems and dried in thin layers. The drug has a spicy smell and a bitter aromatic taste and comes mostly from cultivated plants.
Ingredients: Common wormwood contains 0.5−1 per cent ethereal oil and the bitter ingredient absinthin which transforms into anabsinthin during drug processing. The ethereal oil consists mainly of thujon and thujol. It also contains bitter proazulene artabsin, flavone compounds and lactone.
Uses: The drug is prescribed as an aromatic bitter principle for loss of appetite and digestion complaints, as a carminative and to encourage the secretion of bile. Wormwood is also used as a spice and in the manufacture of vermouth. Only the non-poisonous bitter ingredient and traces of the ethereal oil are used in vermouth. Wormwood foliage is also used to drive away moths, bugs and parasites.
Side effects: The toxic effect of the thujone contained in the ethereal oil can, by misuse for abortion purposes or by using excessive doses of this unreliable drug, lead to fatal poisoning. Vermouth brandy, which can cause serious damage to the central nervous system, has been prohibited in Germany since 1923.
History: Wormwood is one of the oldest medicinal plants. It was mentioned in the papyrus of Ebers (1550 BC). Dioscorides and Galen mention the plant, which was often used in the Middle Ages.

Wormwood

MUGWORT
Artemisia vulgaris L.

Family: Compositae.
Description: This 1–1½ m (3–5 ft) high herbaceous perennial has a many-headed branched rootstock but does not grow any stolons or overwintering rosettes, but several upright, round, grooved, paniculate branched stems, which die back each year. The coarse 5-10 cm (2-4 in) long stout leaves are often slightly rolled at the edge and white felted beneath. The ovate shortly pedicellated flower heads occur in large numbers in a much-branched panicle which is interleaved by lanceolate bracts. The yellow to red-brown flowers scarcely jut out from the scaly hull. The whole plant has a distinctive smell.
Flowering time: Mid summer to early autumn or fall.
Habitat: Mugwort grows particularly on nutrient-rich sand, gravel and loamy soils, and colonises nitrate-rich wasteland. It is also grown as a herb on smallholdings.
Distribution: The plant can be found over almost the whole of the Northern Hemisphere and in North and Central America, as well as Central Asia where probably the whole group and its many sub-species originated.
Parts used: Herbage (Herba Artemisiae).
Harvesting time: Mid-summer to early autumn or fall.
Harvesting instructions: 60-70 cm (24-27 in) of the flowering herbage is cut off, bundled and dried. The drug has a pleasant spicy smell and an aromatic, slightly bitter taste.
Ingredients: Herba Artemisiae contains bitter constituent, tannin and 0.03 to 0.3 per cent ethereal oil with cineol as the main constituent, while thujon is only represented in traces.
Uses: The drug is now rarely used as an aromatic bitter for loss of appetite, digestion and stomach complaints, or as a carminative. Mugwort is one of the strongly aromatic spice herbs used particularly with meat dishes, especially fatty roast goose, whose taste and digestibility it improves.
Side effects: In the past the plant was used in gynaecology, but effective doses are toxic.
History: In antiquity, mugwort was often used for dropsy, epilepsy and bites by poisonous animals. In the Middle Ages the plant played a part in superstition.

Mugwort

ASARABACCA   *Asarum europaeum* L.

Family: Aristolochiaceae.

Description: The thin creeping rhizome of this evergreen plant is jointed and branched. Each spring new leaf shoots appear which are tufted with hair like the other parts of the plant, and can also grow roots. Each foliage shoot carries three or four brownish-green, scale-like leaflets and two kidney-shaped, leathery, petiolated dark-green leaves, whose stems are often shaded reddish-brown. At the end of the shoots there are inconspicuous flowers on short pedicels. The tripartite corolla is dark purple inside and brownish to flesh-coloured outside. The fruit is a six-celled, many-seeded capsule. The flowers smell of pepper when being ground.

Flowering time: Spring.

Habitat: Asarabacca prefers chalky soil and can be found in shady places from the plains right up into the mountains.

Distribution: Asarabacca is the only representative of the Aristolochiaceae in Central Europe. The plant is widespread in Southern and Central Europe and also in the East in Asia Minor and Siberia. Its northern boundary is in England and Southern Sweden but it is rare in large parts of northern Central Europe especially in the west and is missing from the whole of the northern plain.

Parts used: Root (Rhizoma Asari).

Harvesting time: Late summer.

Harvesting instructions: The useful parts must be dried quickly and stored in airtight tins. The drug has a camphor-like smell and a strong spicy, bitter taste. After being stored for a long period the taste and smell disappear as the asaron evaporates.

Ingredients: Rhizoma asari contains 0.7−4 per cent ethereal oil with approximately 40 per cent asarone, and also tannin, starch and resin, and flavonoids.

Uses: Asarabacca was the most important emetic until the beginning of the eighteenth century but was then replaced by ipecac (Radix Ipecacuanhae). Asaron irritates the gastric mucous membrane which leads to reflex vomiting. In France the drug was added to wine. It is classed as a good expectorant medicine, so extracts are used for respiratory troubles.

Side effects: Asarabacca is no longer used as an emetic and diuretic because of its toxic side effects. Poisonings are rare, but if misused for abortion purposes it can have fatal consequences.

History: The drug was often used in antiquity and the Middle Ages. The plant was mentioned by Galen, Pliny and Abbess Hildegard of Bingen (1098-1179).

Asarabacca

†DEADLY NIGHTSHADE   *Atropa belladonna* L.

Family: Solanaceae.
Description: This ½ to 2 m (1½−6½ ft) high perennial has a thick cylindrical rootstock by means of which it survives for several years. The pendulous pedicellated flowers are carried individually in the leaf axils of the upright stems. The bell-shaped corolla is brown-violet on the outside, inside a dirty yellow and veined purple. The five-part calyx increases in size as the fruit ripens to become star-shaped. It encloses the fruit, a shiny black juicy berry, about the size of a cherry.
Flowering time: Summer.
Habitat: Deadly nightshade is generally a shade-loving plant. It prefers humusy soil in beechwoods and forest clearings. It grows up to the 1650 m (5400 ft) contour in the Alps.
Distribution: The plant is distributed across Southern, Central and Western Europe, in the East from the Caucasus to Iran and Asia Minor as well as North Africa. It was also imported into North America.
Parts used: Herbage (Herba Belladonnae), Root (Radix Belladonnae).
Harvesting time: Herbage early to mid-summer, roots Summer.
Harvesting instructions: The longitudinally split roots and herbage were dried as quickly as possible at 50−60°C. The roots are odourless, the fresh herbage has a faint narcotic smell, but when dried is also odourless. The roots taste sweet at first, but later sharp and bitter like the herbage.
Beware! All parts of the deadly nightshade are poisonous!
Ingredients: The drug contains 0.2−1 per cent alkaloid; L-hyoscyamin represents the main alkaloid. Furthermore it contains atropin, as well as small quantities of scopolamin, apoatropin, belladonnin, tropin and scopin. When drying the L-hyoscyamin, it partially transforms into the practically ineffective D-hyoscyamin. The resulting substance is atropin.
Uses: The atropin and drug extracts are used medically. They are primarily anti-convulsive: the smallest dose inhibits glandular secretions and dilates the pupils of the eyes. It is prescribed, mostly in combination for stomach and intestinal cramp, gall-bladder and bladder cramp, as well as for colic, bronchial asthma and whooping cough, stomach ulcers, against vomiting, excessive salivation, night sweats, as an antidote for various kinds of poisoning and externally as eye drops.
Toxic effect: Vomiting is followed by tachycardia, dilation of the pupils, a state of excitement and loss of consciousness and sometimes death through difficulty in breathing. The fatal dose of atropin is 0.1 gram.
History: In the fifteenth century only its poisonous effect was mentioned. In the Middle Ages "witch ointments" contained alkaloids from Solanaceae, and in the eighteenth century deadly nightshade was often used medicinally. Atropin was isolated in 1831.

Deadly Nightshade

†BARBERRY   *Berberis vulgaris* L.

Family: Berberidaceae.

Description: The barberry is a shrub up to 3 m (10 ft) high. Some of the leaves on its long shoots have been transformed into single or up to sevenfold thorns. The oval leaves arise from the axils of the thorns on short bushy shoots. The yellow flowers form many-flowered, hanging clusters and exude a strong unpleasant smell. The ovary develops into a longish, scarlet-red berry with a sour taste.

Flowering time: Mid-spring to early summer.

Habitat: The barberry can be found in dry, sunny places, stony hillsides, in hedgerows of fields and byways and at less damp locations on riverbanks. It is also grown in gardens and parks and can then grow wild. As this shrub is the intermediate host of the highly destructive wheat rust disease, the once abundant barberry shrubs were greatly reduced by grubbing.

Distribution: Barberry grows over most of Europe apart from Northern Scandinavia and the northern parts of Russia. In the south-east it reaches the Caucasus.

Parts used: Fruit(Fructus Berberidis).

Harvesting time: Early autumn or fall.

Harvesting instructions: The fruit were spread in a loose layer on a sheet to dry. They are odourless and have a pleasant but sour and slightly astringent taste.

Ingredients: The drug contains plenty of fruit acids, chelidonic acid, vitamin C, various sugars, pectin, as well as mucin and colouring in contrast to the root cortex and the alkaloid bererine.

Uses: The fruits were formerly used as a mild laxative. They are also used in preparing syrups for flavour correction. The root cortex, Cortex Radicis Berberidis, which contains up to 8 per cent alkaloids, of which berberine is the chief, was used for liver and gall-bladder trouble and kidney stones, as a haemostatic agent for uterine bleeding after child birth and for painful menstrual bleeding.

Side effects: While the fruits are not poisonous, barberry can be dangerous, as an overdose of the root extract can result in poisoning. Small doses of berberine excite the breathing centre, high doses can cause cramp leading to fatal paralysis of the lungs.

History: It is assumed that this plant was used in antiquity. Detailed descriptions of the various parts of the plant appeared in herbals during the Middle Ages.

Barberry

SILVER BIRCH   *Betula pendula* ROTH

Family: Betulaceae.

Description: The silver birch can grow up to 30 m (98 ft) high. In early life its trunk and branches are covered in snow-white bark which often peels off in horizontal strips and in older trees changes into hard black bark. The finer ends of the shoots often hang down. The male and female sex organs are borne separately on all silver birches in spike-like inflorescence. The males are at the ends of the shoots and the females lower down at the ends of shorter side branches. They are pollinated by the wind. The common birch (B. pubescens EHRH.) differs from the silver birch by the fluffy hair on its young twigs and the absence of resin glands typical of the silver birch's young twigs.

Flowering time: Mid to late spring.

Habitat: Silver birch is often found in dry places in deciduous and coniferous woods, on the edges of woods and heathland, while the common birch prefers damp areas in bogland and marshes.

Distribution: The silver birth grows from Europe through Asia to Japan. Its northern boundary in Europe is Central Scandinavia and Lapland. In the south it grows mainly in the mountains. The common birch grows as far north as North Cape, the White Sea and Greenland but is missing from the mountains of Southern Europe.

Parts used: Leaves (Folia Betulae).

Harvesting time: Late spring to mid-summer.

Harvesting instructions: Birch leaves stripped from the branches are dried in the dark, turned over several times, then stored in airtight containers to protect them from light. They have a weak, aromatic smell and a slightly bitter taste.

Ingredients: The drug probably contains saponins, approximately 2 per cent flavonoid glycoside with hyperosid, approximately 0.1 per cent ethereal oil, and phenolic compounds such as tannin, sugar and resins.

Uses: Experiments proved that birch leaves have a very strong diuretic effect without irritating the kidneys (as juniper berries do). The drug is prescribed mainly for kidney and gall bladder complaints. In contrast its use for rheumatism, gout and as a diaphoretic is subsidiary.

Side effects: The drug is harmless.

History: As a North European tree the silver birch was often used in medicine by the peoples who settled there and certainly played a part in superstition.

Silver Birch

BLACK MUSTARD *Brassica nigra* (L.) KOCH

Family: Cruciferae Brassicae.

Description: The thin spindle-shaped root generally produces a 1 m (3 ft), sometimes 2 m (6½ ft) high stem, branched at the base, but straight with branchlets towards the top. All foliage is petiolated. The flowers are grouped together at the ends of the pedicels or side shoots in bushy inflorescences but are more loosely arranged lower down. The petals, about double the length of the calyx, are brilliant yellow. The ovary develops into 2-3 cm (½-1 in) long, small rectangular pod with small round red-brown seeds.

Flowering time: Early summer to early autumn or fall.

Habitat: Black mustard can sometimes be found on riverbanks, in riverside thickets, on waste ground and damp fields, etc. Everywhere it seems to grow as a cultivated plant that has gone wild.

Distribution: The original home of this plant is uncertain. It is scattered across South-west, Southern and Central Europe and eastwards to Afghanistan and Tibet. Nowadays black mustard grows mainly in man-made environments and is cultivated and grows wild in Scandinavia, North and South America, East Asia, Australia and their neighbouring islands.

Parts used: Seeds (Semen Sinapis).

Harvesting time: Mid-summer to early autumn or fall.

Harvesting instructions: Mustard seeds must be dried in a well ventilated place and closely watched because they are liable to fungus attack. When dried they are odourless but taste sharp and burning.

Ingredients: Apart from approximately 30 per cent fatty oil the drug contains, as the most important constituent, 1−5 per cent of the mustard oil glycoside sinigrin, which, when the seed which also contains the enzyme myrosinase is ground down in the presence of water, releases the volatile and strongly irritating allylisothiocyanate (mustard oil).

Uses: The drug is used externally as an irritant for rheumatism, bronchitis, pain in the joints, neuralgia and pleurisy. As table mustard it stimulates the appetite, promotes the secretion of the digestive glands and acts as a digestant.

Side effects: When an excessive does of mustard oil is used externally it produces dermatitis and eventually the complete destruction of the tissue. Internally it causes intolerable pain, cramps, kidney damage and in certain circumstances coma and death.

History: Mustard seeds were known as a medicine and spice in antiquity and were used in the Middle Ages. Mustard oil was first introduced by Boerhaave in 1730.

Black Mustard

MARIGOLD   *Calendula officinalis* L.

Family: Compositae.

Description: The Marigold is an annual, rarely biennial plant up to 50 cm (20 in) high which has a distinctive smell and a spindle-shaped root with fibrous branches. The leaves alternate on the upright, slightly branched stem. The 2–5 cm (½-2 in) wide flower heads are carried singly on leafed stalks. The 15–20 mm long ray florets are golden to orange-yellow, the same colour as the many little tubular disc florets inside the composite flower. The seeds are noticeably bent inwards, the innermost ones are rolled up with grooves on the back.

Flowering time: Early summer to mid-autumn or fall.

Habitat: The marigold is an old cultivated and ornamental plant which even nowadays is grown agriculturally to provide the drug.

Distribution: This plant's native area is probably Southern Europe. It flourishes also in the rugged climate of Finland and even on the plateau of the Pamirs, where, as in this country, it is popular as a garden plant. It is possible that this plant has never existed as a wild form.

Parts used: Flowers (Flores Calendulae)

Harvesting time: Summer.

Harvesting instructions: The drug is collected without the stem when the tongue-like flower is fully open and is then dried in a thin layer at temperatures up to 35°C. It has an unpleasant smell of balsam and a bitter aromatic taste.

Ingredients: Apart from 0.02 per cent volatile oil, the flower of the marigold contains mainly saponins, bitter constituents, flavonoids, carotinoids, pigments, xantophyll, flavone glycosides, triferpen-alcohol, acids and amongst others, mucin and resins.

Uses: The drug has a similar effect to arnica flowers but without causing skin irritation, and is prescribed for external use because of its anti-inflammatory and granulation-promoting properties in the treatment of sores associated with slowly healing wounds and ulcers, effusions of blood, bruises, as a lotion and for compresses, as well as in dentistry. On rare occasions it is prescribed for internal use for expelling bile (cholagogue) and as a cramp-relieving agent.

Side effects: No side effects have been experienced from using the drug.

History: Theophrastus and Dioskorides both mention a drug "Klymenon" which is most probably identical with our marigold. Virgil described this plant as "Caltha luteola". It is described as "Ringula" in the writings of Abbess Hildegard of Bingen, which detail its medicinal effects.

Marigold

HEATHER (LING)   *Calluna vulgaris* (L.) HULL.

Family: Ericaceae.

Description: Heather (ling) is a branched evergreen shrublet 20—80 cm (8—31 in) high. It has prostrate rooting shoots and ascending branches. The thin grey-brown stems are densely covered with upright branches. The linear-lanceolate 1—3.5 mm long leaves overlap like shingles. The one-sided clustered inflorescence is densely covered in flowers. The slightly nodding, reddish, rarely white, flowers with short pedicels and strawy violet-pink calces grow on short shoots.

Flowering time: Mid-summer to mid-autumn or fall.

Habitat: Heather grows in poor soil lacking in nutrients and is widespread on moorland, in light dry woods and covers large areas in the North West of Germany particularly. In the Alps it stays below the snow line.

Distribution: The plant is particularly widespread in Western Europe but not in the Mediterranean. It even occurs in Morocco and the Azores. To the east, the area extends across Asia Minor to Western Siberia. In the north it grows in northern Norway and Iceland but is not a native of Atlantic North America.

Parts used: Herbage with flowers (Herba Callunae).

Harvesting time: Late summer to early autumn or fall.

Harvesting instructions: The flowers, together with the leaves, are stripped off by hand or cut off. The woody parts are not gathered. The material to be used is laid out in thin layers to dry and must not lose its violet colour. The drug has an aromatic smell and tastes bitter sweet.

Ingredients: Heather contains the hydrochinon glycoside arbutin (0.3—0.4 per cent), the flavonglycosides quercitrin and myricitrin, as well as tannin, resins and traces of ethereal oils.

Uses: The drug is prescribed as a diuretic because of its flavonoid content. Its antiseptic effect in kidney and gall bladder complaints is debatable, because it contains only a small amount of arbutin. The tannin content of heather explains its effectiveness against diarrhoea.

Side effects: No side effects are known.

History: The heather mentioned by Dioscorides is probably a drier (*Erica arborea*). *Calluna vulgaris* was mentioned in the Middle Ages in many writings, especially in connection with stomach and intestinal complaints.

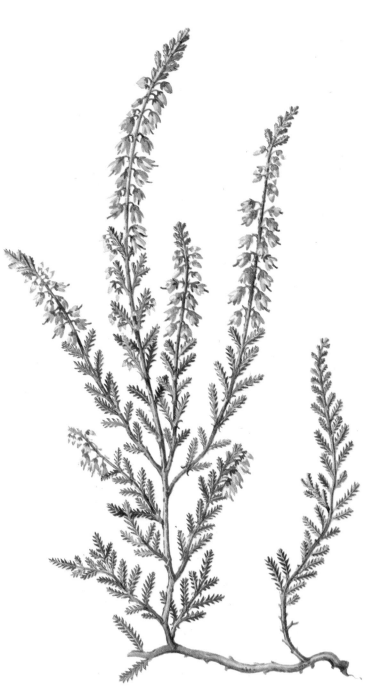

Heather (Ling)

SHEPHERD'S PURSE
Capsella bursa-pastoris (L.) MED.

Family: Cruciferae Brassicae.

Description: Shepherd's purse is one of the annuals that survive the winter i.e plants that germinate in the autumn survive the winter and die the following summer after they have flowered and borne fruit. But they can flower and fruit the whole year, though not during severe frosty periods. The basal foliage forms a multi-leaved rosette and the shape and size of the leaves can vary quite dramatically. The flowers first form a crowded umbellate inflorescence which then stretches out into a long cluster. The small flowers are white and inconspicuous. During flowering the tiny ovary develops the well-known many-seeded pod borne on a small horizontal petiole on the floral axis.

Flowering time: It is only interrupted during long periods of frost.

Habitat: Being so undemanding, shepherd's purse is one of our most widespread plants. It is found on all soils, from the coast to the mountains. It grows in fields, on pathways, waste ground, pastures, by the sea and on river banks.

Distribution: This plant, now found on cultivated ground all over the world, often introduced, seems to have originated in the Mediterranean area. In Europe its distribution reaches as far north as North Cape and Iceland.

Parts used: Herbage (Herba Bursae pastoris).

Harvesting time: Late spring to late summer.

Harvesting instructions: Herbage and flowers collected from plants grown in dry areas and dried quickly. Leaves damaged by parasites should be discarded. When the plant is fresh it has a weak unpleasant odour which disappears when dried and a sharp bitter taste.

Ingredients: The shepherd's purse contains biogene amines such as cholin, acetylcholin, hystamine and tyramin. Furthermore, flavonoids such as diosmin, tannin and resins, potassium and sodium salts.

Uses: The drug has haemostatic effects. At various times it was used instead of ergot of rye or the Canadian hydrastis root, but it is not as effective as these and unreliable because of its variable ingredients. It is still not known which ingredients produce the effect.

Side effects: No poisoning has occurred.

History: The plant and its medicinal effects were known in antiquity and were often used in the Middle Ages.

Shepherd's Purse

SAND SEDGE   *Carex arenaria* L.

Family: Cyperaceae.
Description: The sand sedge's dark brown rootstock consisting of long fibrous scaly leaf bases, by which the plant survives the winter, can extend up to 10 m (33 ft). It is as strong as a quill and many-branched. The rough triangular stem, sharp towards the top, is about the same length as the leaves 20−40 cm (8−15 in) at flowering time. Its leaves arranged in three ranks on the stems have fairly narrow leaf blades. The inflorescence is usually mainly pendulous and up to 6 cm (2in) long, a spike-shaped panicle tight above but loose below with six to sixteen spikelets. The lower spikelets are formed exclusively of females, the middle ones at the base by females, those at the tips by males and the upper ones exclusively by males. At flowering time their anthers protrude far beyond the subtending leaf, so pollen can be carried to the stigma by the wind.
Flowering time: Late spring to early summer.
Habitat: Sand sedge is mostly at home on sandy soil. It is of great importance for stabilising the dunes on the North Sea and Baltic coasts.
Distribution: The plant can be found in coastal areas of Europe, as well as in Siberia, North America and by the Black Sea, but it is absent from the Arctic. In Central Europe it has penetrated as far inland as Lusatia.
Parts used: Rootstock with rootlets (Rhizoma Caricis).
Harvesting time: Early to mid spring.
Harvesting instructions: The roots are dug out, freed from earth and rootlets, split up if necessary then dried on a line in a shady, well ventilated place. The drug has an aromatic smell when fresh but when dry is odourless. It tastes sweet, pleasant, bitter and scratchy.
Ingredients: The drug contains saponins, approximately 8−10 per cent tannin, resin, mucilage, silicic acid and ethereal oil (traces).
Uses: The rootstock of the sand sedge is also referred to as German sarsaparilla because it has a similar effect to the Central American smilax derived from Radix Sarsaparillae. It was used as a diuretic as well as a blood purifier for bronchitis, gout and rheumatism.
Side effects: No side effects are known.
History: Nothing is known about the use of sand sedge as a medicine in antiquity and the Middle Ages. The drug was first introduced to medicine in the mid-eighteenth century.

Sand Sedge

*STEMLESS CARLINE THISTLE
Carlina acaulis L.

Family: Compositae.

Description: This more or less stemless plant which can grow up to 40 cm (15 in) high survives by means of its vertical root. The leaves of the stemless form are arranged in a rosette. The flower heads generally arise singly from the stem which is often shaded red. With their ray-like involucres they measure between 5 and 15 cm (2—6 in) across. The white to reddish tubular flowers grow to between 12 and 17 mm long. The pappus is twice to three times as long as the roughly 5 mm long fruit.

Flowering time: Mid-summer to early autumn or fall.

Habitat: Although this plant prefers rocky soil, it is found in a variety of soils from the plains to the alpine and high alpine regions, either singly or in groups in light sunny places in thickets, on stony slopes and heaths and in pastures.

Distribution: The stemless carline thistle is widely scattered, though more numerous in some places, in Spain, France, East Germany, West Germany, Austria and Italy, the Danube countries and as far as Central Russia.

Parts used: Root (Radix Carlinae).

Harvesting time: Early to mid-autumn or fall.

Harvesting instructions: The cleaned roots are threaded on strings and dried. Larger pieces must be split longitudinally. The drug has a penetrating, unpleasant smell and a bitter-sweet, sharp, spicy taste.

Ingredients: The root of the stemless carline thistle contains 1—2 per cent ethereal oil of narcotic-like odour which consists mainly of the bacteriologically stable effective carlinaoxide and also carlines. Other constituents are tannin, inulin and resin.

Uses: These are limited to folk medicine. Here the drug is used mainly as a stomachic, diuretic and sudorific, as well as a vermicide.

Side effects: The practical use of the bactericidal effects of the carlinaoxides contrasts with its toxicity and instability.

History: The stemless carline thistle is not found in Greece so it was unknown to medicine in antiquity. It has been used as a drug in folk medicine since the Middle Ages.

Stemless Carline Thistle

CARAWAY

Carum carvi L.

Family: Apiaceae Umbelliferae.
Description: This 30 to 100 cm (12−39 in) high biennial plant has a finger-thick, usually spindle-shaped root, with a carroty smell. In its second year the plant develops erect, square-grooved stem branches right from the base and bearing isolated feathery leaves. The medium sized umbels each consist of about eight to sixteen smaller umbels. The petals of the flowers are white to red. The schizocarp grows 4−5 mm long and when ripe splits into the two familiar rather sickle-shaped partial fruits.
Flowering time: Late spring to mid-summer.
Habitat: Caraway is primarily found in meadows after the first cut. It also grows in pastures, by footpaths and on waste ground. It can be found on cattle tracks high up in the mountains.
Distribution: This old spice plant is spread throughout Northern and Central Europe. It grows wild in various parts of Europe and is also cultivated, particularly in Holland. Further afield it can be found in Siberia, the Caucasus, the Himalayas, in North Africa, North America and New Zealand. It is quite common in Germany, where it is cultivated too.
Parts used: Fruits (Fructus Carvi).
Harvesting time: Early to mid-summer.
Harvesting instructions: The fruits are harvested before they are fully ripe as later they easily drop off. They quickly ripen when dried in a well ventilated place. The drug has a distinctive strong warm, spicy smell and sometimes a burning taste.
Ingredients: Caraway fruits contain ethereal oil (approximately 3−7 per cent) which contains carvon and limones, fatty oil with linoleic and oleic as well as petroselenic acid.
Uses: The fruits and ethereal oil are often used as a carminative, stomachic and choleretic because of their anti-spasmodic properties. The drug has a calming effect on the stomach, stimulates the appetite, promotes digestion and increases digestive secretions in the digestive system. As an additive to foods that are difficult to digest like cabbage, cheese and fresh bread caraway was used not only to improve the flavour as *Kummel* (brandy) was thought of as a preventive medicine against colic. Sometimes the oil was used externally as a linament against skin parasites.
Side effects: Poisoning from this fruit is unknown.
History: The drug has played a part as a medicine and spice since the early Middle Ages.

Caraway

CORNFLOWER
Centaurea cyanus L.

Family: Compositae.

Description: The cornflower is an annual or biennial plant, 20 to 70 cm (8−29 in) high with a spindle-shaped taproot. It has an upright, angular, usually many-branched stem. The roughly 3 cm (1 in) wide flowers are borne singly at the ends of the shoots and consist exclusively of tubular florets. The greatly enlarged terminal funnel-shaped florets are sexless and serve like the ray florets of the sunflower purely for display. The outer and inner flowers are an intense blue.

Flowering time: Early summer to early autumn or fall.

Habitat: The plant is a widespread weed in German cornfields. It occurs less frequently in potato and beet fields.

Distribution: The cornflower, originally only at home in the Eastern Mediterranean, spread along with the cultivation of grain. Seeds of this plant have been found in the remains of Bronze Age lake dwellings. But it has still not become part of our native flora so it can only be found on arable land. It is distributed in India, North America, Australia and North Africa and can even be found in South America.

Parts used: Flowers (Flores Cyani).

Harvesting time: Summer.

Harvesting instructions: The flowers are collected without their calyces and dried quickly in the shade so they retain their colour and stored protected from light. They are odourless and have a sweet, slightly salty taste.

Ingredients: The drug contains the bitter ingredient centaurine, the glycoside cichoriin, the anthocyan colouring cyanine and tannin, resin and mucilage.

Uses: Cornflower blossoms were formerly used as a diuretic. Nowadays they are almost exclusively used as a decorative ingredient in various tea mixtures and to a lesser extent as aromatic bitters to aid indigestion.

Side effects: The drug has no side effects.

History: It is assumed that the plant Abbess Hildegard of Bingen described as "Centaurea" was the cornflower.

Cornflower

CENTAURY
(C. umbellatum).

Centaurium minus MOENCH

Family: Gentianaceae.
Description: This glabrous annual or biennial plant reaches a height of 10 to 50 cm (4—20 in) and has a light-coloured taproot. The simple, upright, rectangular stem branches towards the top. The lower foliage forms a basal rosette. The bracts are arranged cross-wise in opposite pairs. The odourless herbage has a strong bitter taste. The five-petalled rose-red flowers form a cymose inflorescence and the small individual umbels are arranged on long stems in the leaf axils.
Flowering time: Mid-summer to early autumn or fall.
Habitat: The widespread centaury grows in clearways, warm bare grassy areas, in light undergrowth, round the edges of fields, on arable land and in dune valleys. It can be found on flat land up to a height of 1400 m (4600 ft) or so.
Distribution: This plant grows over almost the whole of Europe apart from its most northerly areas. To the east it is found in the Caucasus to Iran and in the south as far as North Africa. It was probably introduced into North America.
Parts used: Herbage (Herba Centaurii).
Harvesting time: Early summer to early autumn or fall.
Harvesting instructions: The aerial parts of the plant are cut off about 5 cm (2 in) above the ground while in flower, tied in small bunches and hung up to dry. The drug is odourless and has a lingering bitter taste.
Ingredients: The main ingredient of the centaury is the bitter constituent gentiopicrosid and erythaurin. Other ingredients are nicotinic acid compounds and oleanolic acid.
Uses: Like yellow gentian, the drug is a pure aromatic bitter (bitter value 200—3500). It stimulates the secretions and peristaltis of the intestinal tract, stimulates the appetite and promotes digestion. It is therefore included in liver, gall-bladder and stomach decoctions. In the past it was used for many other complaints.
Side effects: No side effects are known.
History: Centaury is an old medicinal plant which was used by the followers of Hippocrates for chest complaints. Dioscorides and Galen refer to the plant as *"Kentaurion to mikron"*; Pliny called it *"fel terrae"*, meaning "earth bile", referring to its bitter taste.

Centaury

ICELAND MOSS   *Cetraria islandica* (L.) ACH.

Family: Parmeliaceae.

Description: Like all lichens this plant results from a living partnership between a higher fungus and an alga. It has an upright, bushy thallus up to 10 cm (4 in) high with leaf-like lobates. The small, dish-like fruits (apothecia) form after some years and only appear on the upper side of the lobe end. The inner part of the thallus, the medulla, consists of a loose mycelium and contains lichen starch. Despite its bitter taste the lichen serves as food for animals and people in times of need in Arctic countries by reason of its lichenin content.

Habitat: Iceland moss is found from the lowlands to the high mountains. This lichen is fairly common in woodland, especially coniferous woods, on sandy heath, and in boggy soils and areas of short grass.

Distribution: Iceland moss is well distributed in the northern parts of Europe, Asia and North America and even grows in Anarctica. In northern Central Europe it is found on the plain, further south mainly in moderately high mountains and in the Alps.

Parts used: Whole plant (Lichen Islandicus).

Harvesting time: Mid-spring to mid-autumn or fall.

Harvesting instructions: After any contaminated or damaged plants have been removed the lichen is spread out in thin layers in the sunshine to dry. The drug has a distinctive smell and tastes bitter with a slimy texture.

Ingredients: Islandic moss contains more than 50 per cent mucin plus lichenin which is soluble in hot water and the isolichenin which is soluble in cold water. Furthermore the drug contains approximately 2 per cent of bitter tasting furmaric protocetrar acid and protolichesterin acid, with some iodine.

Uses: The drug is used because of its lichen acid content on the one hand as aromatic bitter to stimulate the appetite and promote digestion, and on the other hand as a mucus membrane coating agent for coughs and gastro-intestinal inflammations. It has been used externally for slow healing wounds and in folk medicine was formerly used against tuberculosis.

Side effects: No side effects are known.

History: Iceland moss has been known as a food in Nordic countries since the earliest times. Linnaeus recommended the medical use of the drug, which was a key medicine at the end of the eighteenth century. In eastern countries it was used to manufacture alcohol.

Iceland Moss

†GREATER CELANDINE *Chelidonium majus* L.

Family: Papaveraceae.

Description: The greater celandine is a 30—50 cm (12—20 in) high perennial plant that survives by means of its roots. The upright, branched stem, like all the other parts of the plant, contains orange-coloured sap. The undersides of the leaves and the stems are covered in a milky light bluish-green rime. Part of the tender foliage forms a basal rosette. The flowers are arranged in umbels each of 2—6 flowers. The petals, like the many stamens, are brilliant yellow. The ovary develops into a 5 cm (2 in) long, pod-like capsule, containing oval black seeds.

Flowering time: Late spring to early autumn or fall.

Habitat: The greater celandine prefers to colonise places near human settlements. It can often be found beside paths and roads, along hedgerows, fences, on waste ground, in scrub and also in cracks in walls where ants have brought the seeds.

Distribution: The plant grows throughout Europe. In the East it can be found in the more temperate and coldest parts of Asia. It is an introduced plant in Atlantic North America.

Parts used: Herbage (Herba Chelidonii).

Harvesting time: Mid-spring to early summer.

Harvesting instructions: The herbage, collected before flowering, is either used fresh or quickly dried between 60 and 70°C. It has a narcotic smell, lost when it is dried, and a bitter taste.

Beware! The drug is very rich in alkaloids and the yellow milky sap secreted from the plant is a strong skin irritant.

Ingredients: From the milky sap of the drug, more than 20 alkaloids have already been isolated. The main alkaloid is chelidonin, others are chelerythrin, sanguinarin, berberine, protopin and spartein, saponin, carotenoid pigments and enzymes.

Uses: The combined extracts of the drug have a basically calming and antispasmodic effect and also stimulate the bile. It is prescribed for liver and gall-bladder complaints and for cramps in the gastro-intestinal tract. The drug was formerly used for gout, rheumatism, angina pectoris and neuralgia. In folk medicine the fresh milky sap was used against warts.

Toxic effect: Its strong irritant effect manifests itself in cases of poisoning by burning skin, pain and blisters forming in the mouth and throat, stomachache, vomiting, bloody diarrhoea, kidney damage, circulatory disorder, collapse and even death.

History: The greater celandine was used in antiquity.

Greater Celandine

†ERGOT   *Claviceps purpurea* (L.) TULASNE

Class: Ascomycetes.

Description: The blue to dark-purple, straight or slightly bent, sausage-shaped bodies called ergot occur mainly in the ears of rye and are 4 cm (1½ in) long and 3−4 mm wide. They appear between the glumes in place of normal grains and, like them, have white seeds inside. Ergot is not a product of the cereal plant but the permanent form (sclerotium) of a fungus.

Habitat: Ergot is found mostly in rye but it sometimes occurs on wheat and barley ears as well as on some wild grasses.

Parts used: Whole grains (Secale cornutum).

Harvesting time: Early summer to early autumn or fall.

Harvesting instructions: The sclerotia that have grown on the rye then dropped off are collected during dry weather and dried in a little warmth. They have a musty smell and an insipid offensive taste.

Beware! Ergot is very poisonous!

Ingredients: The most important ingredients of ergot of rye are the alkaloids which are divided into the water soluble group of ergometrin or ergobasin and into the water insoluble of ergotamin and ergotoxin. Other ingredients are pigments and histamine.

Uses: Due to the variable alkaloid content, between 0.025 and 0.2 per cent, drug extracts are no longer used. Nowadays only industrially isolated alkaloids are used in prepared medicines used in obstetrics, for migraines and also in various compound medicines.

Toxic effects: Ergot poisoning can manifest itself as a "burning epidemic" (Ergotismus gangraenosus) which results in a restricted circulation in the limbs with severe burning pains ("holy fire"). The limbs subsequently turn black and drop off from lack of blood. Alternatively, poisoning can affect the nervous system, of which the symptoms are "cramp epidemic" (Ergotismus convulsivus) accompanied by itching (itching sickness), thirst and ravenous hunger, cramp in the flexor muscles and finally death.

History: Ergot was formerly assumed to be a mis-shapen grain and was ground down. In 1782 Johann Taube recognised its toxicity as the cause of "itching sickness". The biology of the ergot fungus was revealed by Tulasne in 1852.

Ergot

†AUTUMN CROCUS   *Colchicum autumnale* L.

Family: Liliaceae.

Description: The plant survives the winter with two bulbs, one of which is filled with a reserve of nutrients during summer. The offshoot of the parent bulb, which has already formed a flower in the autumn, then thickens up during the winter to form a second bulb, while the parent bulb shrinks. Each plant develops one to three pale lilac flowers without calyces. The corolla is funnel-shaped and grows downwards into a long tube to reach the bulb which is often 15−20 cm (6−8 in) under the ground. Close above this is the trilocular ovary which remains in the ground during the winter. In spring, the pedicel, which was very short at flowering time, stretches up and in this way brings the young fruit above ground where it develops into an ovate capsule.

Flowering time: Late summer to mid-autumn or fall.

Habitat: The autumn crocus prefers damp places, particularly meadows, and grows from the lowlands right up into the mountains. When it becomes too numerous in meadows, it is a terrible weed.

Distribution: This plant is found in Southern, Central and Western Europe and the southern part of Russia. In the North it grows in Ireland, England and Southern Sweden.

Parts used: Seeds (Semen Colchici).

Harvesting time: Late spring to mid-summer.

Harvesting instructions: The drug is collected before the seeds are fully ripe, when the capsules are yellowish-brown in colour and dried in the shade with a little heat. The seeds then ripen and can easily be removed from the open capsules. They are odourless and have a bitter, sharp, rough, offensive taste.
Beware! The drug is very poisonous!

Ingredients: The autumn crocus contains 0.2−0.6 per cent colchicin, has an alkaloid-like compound in the seed (phytosterol, sugar) and the main ingredient in the bulb is demecolcin and colchicosid.

Uses: In medicine drug extracts of colchicine but more often the less poisonous demecolcin and the semi-synthetic colchicin derivative are used for gout, particularly for acute attacks. Its effectiveness can be traced to its intervention into the metabolism of purines. Demecolcin is used alone for its cell-growth limiting effects in some cases of leukaemia and externally for skin cancers. Colchicin is used in plant cultivation for obtaining polyploidal species.

Toxic effects: Only a few hours after being poisoned, there is scratching and burning in the throat, cholera-like diarrhoea, paralysis of the central nervous system and death due to paralysis of the breathing apparatus. 20 mg of colchicin or 5 g of the seeds form a fatal dose.

History: The plant has been used in medicine since the beginning of the seventeenth century.

Autumn Crocus

†HEMLOCK   *Conium maculatum* L.

Family: Umbelliferae.

Description: This annual or biennial plant has an offensive smell. It has whitish spindle-shaped root branches. The ½ to 2½ m (1½−8 ft) high upright tubular stem is finely grooved and covered in a bluish bloom which can be wiped off. The lower part is often covered with red specks. The dark to grey-green, pinnatifid leaves are fairly limp. Of the flat, short-stemmed flower umbels the side ones are slightly taller than those at the apex. The stamens are nearly twice as long as the five petals of the white flowers.

Flowering time: Early summer to early autumn or fall.

Habitat: Hemlock is usually found near human settlements in hedgerows, walls, fences, footpaths and on arable and wasteland.

Distribution: Hemlock is a native of Central Europe, Norway and Finland, in Asia to the Altai and Baikal region, in North Africa to Ethiopia. In the East it is mainly a mountain plant. Hemlock has also become established in Eastern North America as well as Central and South America.

Parts used: Herbage with flowers (Herba Conii).

Harvesting time: Mid to late summer.

Harvesting instructions: The leaves and flowering tips of the stem are collected and must be dried very quickly. The drug smells unpleasant like mouse urine and has an offensive and sharp bitter taste.

Beware! All parts of the plant, particularly the fruit, are highly poisonous!

Ingredients: The drug contains alkaloids of the piperidin type; the main alkaloid is coniin.

Uses: The drug which was sometimes used in the past as an antispasmodic and analgesic is now no longer used medicinally because of its high toxicity and therefore its limited therapeutic value.

Toxic effects: Poisoning can occur by mistaking the root for horse-radish root, the leaves for parsley or the fruits for anise or fennel. The alkaloids work very quickly, paralysing the motor centres (neuro-muscular junctions). 0.5 to 1 g coniin is a fatal dose.

History: In antiquity hemlock was used for carrying out death sentences (Socrates) and, mixed with opium, was used as a suicide poison handed out by the government. Death occurs while fully conscious, by paralysing the breathing muscles. Coniin was isolated from the plant in 1831.

Hemlock

FIELD LARKSPUR   *Delphinium consolida* L.

Family: Ranunculaceae.

Description: This larkspur is a 20 to 60 cm (8−24 in) high annual plant with a short, brownish taproot. Its upright, many-branched stem bears the three-part, bi- or tripinnatifid slender-tipped foliage. The violet-blue, occasionally pink or white, flowers are borne in loose, often branched clusters, whose pedicels are significantly longer than the subtending leaves in whose axils they originate. The plant is a pure "bumble bee flower" because the nectar secreted at the pointed end of the 15 mm (½ in) long spur can only be reached by bumble bees.

Flowering time: Late spring to late summer.

Habitat: This plant can be found as a weed from the plain to the alpine foothills. It is frequently found on arable land, fallow fields, on banks between fields, in vineyards and on refuse tips.

Distribution: In prehistoric times this larkspur was introduced into Europe from the East with the cultivation of grain crops and can now be found over most of Europe to Scandinavia and the Baltic countries. In the East it reaches from Turkey and Armenia to the Urals.

Parts used: Flowers (Flores Calcatrippae).

Harvesting time: Summer.

Harvesting instructions: The stemless flowers are collected and spread out on a sheet in thin layers to dry in a well ventilated place. The flowers must not be pressed or they will lose their colour. The drug is odourless and has a weak, bitter, astringent taste.

Ingredients: The flowers of the field larkspur contain the blue anthocyanglycoside delphin, camphor oil and quercetin. The herbage of the plant contains the alkaloid calcatrippin, the seed alkaloid delsoline and delcosine.

Uses: In the old days the tincture of the field larkspur was used as a treatment for lice: nowadays, however, it is not used at all in this country.

Toxic effect: Poisoning from this plant is unknown and with its relatively small content of active substances, is highly unlikely.

History: This larkspur was known as a medicinal plant in the Middle Ages and was used as a mild wound healing agent.

Field Larkspur

†LILY OF THE VALLEY   *Convallaria majalis* L.

Family: Liliaceae.

Description: Lily of the valley is a herbaceous perennial that survives by means of its stolon-like, creeping, branched and fairly thin rootstock, which in spring first grows some leaflets which soon decompose, then every second year (also 1-3) produces foliage. The pedicel which has no leaves develops a one-sided cluster of five to thirteen flowers at the top. From the axil of the lanceolate bract emerges a nodding, short-stemmed, strongly scented flower with a calyx. The white petals form a pointed bell-shaped perianth, with six stamens at the base. The ovary develops into a two to six seeded scarlet-red berry with round blue seeds.

Flowering time: Late spring to early summer.

Habitat: Lily of the valley is quite frequently found in light deciduous, more rarely in coniferous woodlands and also in thickets and alpine pastures.

Distribution: Lily of the valley grows wild in the above-mentioned surroundings throughout Europe, with the exception of the extreme northern areas and some areas in the South. Its distribution extends through temperate Asia to Japan. It can also be found in North America.

Parts used: Herbage (Herba Convallariae).

Harvesting time: Late spring.

Harvesting instructions: The herbage and flowers are dried in thin layers and must not be turned. The drug is odourless and has a sweet, bitter, slightly sharp taste.

Beware! This plant is highly poisonous!

Ingredients: The lily of the valley contains 0.2−0.6 per cent of glycoside which is used for treatment of the heart. The main glycosides, whose quantitative share can vary according to the origin of the drug, are convallatoxol, locundjosid and convallosid which transforms when drying into convallatoxin. Other ingredients are saponins, asparagin and chelidonic with other organic acids.

Uses: In some countries medicines containing pure glycosides are used for weak hearts. In isolated cases standardised drug extracts are still used.

Toxic effects: Poisoning is not uncommon and can result particularly from eating the berries, drinking water from a vase containing the flowers or by taking an excessive dose. Poisoning manifests itself as sickness, vomiting, diarrhoea, urinary urgency, dizziness and paralysis and can lead to collapse and death.

History: The drug was first mentioned in the sixteenth century and has never played a significant role in folk medicine.

Lily of the Valley

CORIANDER   *Coriandrum sativum* L.

Family: Umbelliferae.

Description: This annual plant produces a 20—50 cm (8—20 in) long stem, branched towards the top, from its spindle-shaped taproot. The basal foliage dies early. The long-stemmed umbels are formed of three to five rays and are borne in the leaf axils or terminally. The petals are white or reddish. The spherical fruit measures 2—5 mm across. It is brown to straw-yellow when ripe and consists of two partial fruits that hang firmly together.

Flowering time: Early to mid summer.

Habitat: Nowadays this old cultivated plant can only be found on cultivated ground particularly as a weed among crops. In recent times it has been cultivated on a large scale around Kolleda (Thuringia), but the main areas of cultivation are in Southern and Western Europe, in Ethiopia, China and Japan.

Distribution: Coriander probably originated in the Eastern Mediterranean. Nowadays it can often be found in those areas as a weed of crops. But it can also be found growing wild in East Asia as well as North and South America.

Parts used: Seeds (Fructus Coriandri).

Harvesting time: Early to mid summer.

Harvesting instructions: The seeds are collected when they turn brown. The relevant umbels are cut from the plant and spread out to dry on a sheet. Having ripened, the seeds drop out. The drug smells spicy and tastes sweet but when chewed the seeds produce a burning sensation.

Ingredients: The drug contains approximately 1 per cent ethereal oil with linalool, geraniol, borneol, cymol, pines and phellandres.

Uses: Coriander seeds, like kummel (caraway) seeds, were occasionally used because of their ethereal oil content as a stomachic, carminative and antispasmodic medicine. They are also used to improve the flavour of unpleasant-tasting medicines and often as a spice in curry powders, for example, as a spice in cooking and in the liquor industry.

Side effects: No side effects are known.

History: Coriander is an ancient cultivated plant known to have been grown as far back as 1000 BC. Coriander fruits have been found in Egyptian graves dating back to this time. The plant was often referred to in the ancient writings of Mediterranean peoples. Coriander was also mentioned in the "Capitulare" of Charlemagne and in medieval herbals. The oil obtained from the fruit was listed in a Berlin spice appraisal book in 1574.

Coriander

HAWTHORN   *Crataegus oxyacantha (L.)L.*

Family: Rosaceae

Description: Hawthorn usually forms a 2½ to 3 m (8-10 ft) high shrub, rarely a small tree. It has tough hard wood, smooth ash-grey bark and generally thorny twigs. The flowers are borne in many-flowered, upright umbel-like panicles. The very short notched petals are white or pink and the stamens carry red anthers. Each flower generally contains two styles. The red fruit (drupe) is crowned with the remains of the calyx. It contains two or three single-seeded stones.

Flowering time: Late spring.

Habitat: Hawthorn is commonly found in the lowlands and right up into mountainous areas on humus-rich and rocky ground, even where this is rather dry. It is particularly frequent on heavy loamy soil and can be found in deciduous and pine woods, open scrubland, hedges and gardens.

Distribution: This shrub grows in places up to 900 m (2,950 ft) above sea level. In the North it reaches Southern and Central Sweden and into Norway, where it probably only grows wild.

Parts used: Fruit (Fructus Crataegi), flowers (Flores Crataegi).

Harvesting time: Fruits, late summer to mid autumn or fall, flowers, late spring to early summer.

Harvesting instructions: The flowers and leaves are stripped from the branches while the tree is in bloom. Discoloured fruits are not collected. The harvested material is first dried in thin layers in an airy place, then in artificial heat that must not exceed 70 °C. Any flowers that have turned brown should be removd. Flowers and fruit are odourless and taste bitter, the fruit is also sour.

Ingredients: The drug contains mainly flavonoids such as hyperosid, vitexin, vitexin-4-rhamnosid, rutine and triterpene, ursolic and oleanolic acids and tannin.

Uses: Hawthorn preparations have only been used medicinally for a few decades. The drug has a specific effect on the heart, particularly on the ageing and strained heart. It enlarges the coronary vessels, strengthens the heart muscle and has a regulating effect the heart as well as reducing blood pressure. It is prescribed in the form of standardized drug extracts as a tonic for the heart after infectious illnesses and as a blood pressure reducing agent. It is sometimes recommended for deficient cerebral blood circulation.

Side effects: This drug produces no side effects even when used continuously.

History: Hawthorn fruit were only used in the past as cheap food and stewed in times of hardship.

Hawthorn

PUMPKIN
Cucurbita pepo L.

Family: Cucurbitaceae.

Description: The pumpkin is an annual creeping, or with its multiple tendrils, climbing, leafy plant that can reach 10 m (10 yd) long. Its angular, thick stems are covered with stiff hairs and alternate, petiolate, mostly five-lobed leaves. This plant is monoecious i.e. separate male and female flowers grow on the same plant. The brilliant golden yellow bell-shaped corolla is about 7–10 cm (3–4 in) in diameter. The large, orange to greenish, round to longish fruits about 15–40 cm (6–15 in) in diameter have stout, leathery skins and firm fibrous flesh. Inside develop many flat oval seeds, with distinct edges.

Flowering time: Summer.

Habitat: Many kinds of pumpkin and marrow are grown in fields, gardens and on compost heaps.

Distribution: The pumpkin probably originated in tropical Central America. Its distribution in Eurasia followed the discovery of America. But long before that various kinds of pumpkin were cultivated by the American Indians as far north as the Canadian Lakes.

Parts used: Seeds (Semen Cucurbitae).

Harvesting time: Mid-autumn or fall.

Harvesting instructions: The pumpkin seeds are separated from the flesh, spread out on a sheet and dried in the air or over a heater until they are no longer damp. They are odourless and taste of almonds.

Ingredients: The drug contains the usual reserves which are common for seeds especially the so-called cucurbitacine, amino acid, cucurbitin, lecithin and resin.

Uses: The seeds of *Cucurbita pepo*, *C. maxima* and *C. moschata*, which are no longer considered a useful drug, have a specific effect on intestinal worms, attributed to the cucurbitacine. The drug was therefore formerly used against maw-worms and tape worms.

Side effects: The drug has no side effects.

History: What records we have of Greek and Roman medicine and herbals from the Middle Ages give us no reliable clues about the use of pumpkins in medicine.

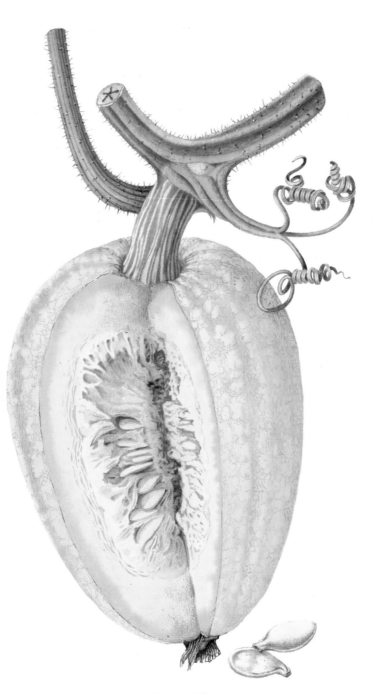

Pumpkin

†MEZEREON   *Daphne mezereum* L.

***Family:** Thymelaeaceae.

Description: The mezereon is a deciduous shrub about 30 to 150 cm (1−5 ft) high. Its branches are very tough and carry leaves only at the tips of the shoots. The initially pink-violet, later slightly fading but rarely white flowers, emerge in stemless clusters in the axils of the previous year's leaves. They open before the foliage appears and give off a strong fragrance. The ovary develops into a brilliant red berry.

Flowering time: Early to mid-spring (at high altitudes until early summer).

Habitat: The mezereon is found mainly in rather shady deciduous woods and occasionally in coniferous woodland. It prefers the outskirts of woods, glens and riverside undergrowth. It particularly likes chalky soil.

Distribution: The mezereon can be found in almost the whole of Europe as far as the east and north of Norway, and further afield in Siberia, the Caucasus and Turkey. Its north-western boundary is the line between Cologne-Hanover and eastern Schleswig-Holstein, but is entirely absent from Brandenburg.

Parts used: Bark (Cortex Mezerei).

Harvesting time: Early spring.

Harvesting instructions: The bark of the main stem and the thicker twigs is collected before the plant blooms. After drying, the rind is rolled up with the inner bark on the outside. The drug loses its effectiveness if stored for a long period of time. It is odourless but tastes sharp and burning after being chewed for a while.

Beware! Mezereon berries and bark are poisonous!

Ingredients: The drug contains amongst others the unpoisonous glycoside daphnin, umbelliferon and the sharp tasting mezereum resin (formerly called mezerein or mezerein acid anhydrid), also daphnin, and the poisonous compound contained in the seed is described as mezerin.

Uses: Mezereon, was formerly used for chronic skin complaints, gout and rheumatism, is now no longer used medicinally.

Toxic effect: External use produces blisters and shedding of the epidermis, and with larger doses, ulcerous disintegration of the skin. Corresponding symptoms follow internal use, which causes serious damage from the lips to the bowels. Apart from local irritation poisoning can follow resorption of the poison which damages the central nervous system, circulation and kidneys. Eating 10 to 12 berries can cause fatal poisoning.

History: Mezereon was already used in antiquity.

Mezereon

†THORN APPLE   *Datura stramonium* L.

Family: Solanaceae.
Description: This 30 to 120 cm (1−4 ft) high annual plant has a white spindly, ramified branched root. The bare upright stem is simple or forked. The leaves have long petioles, the lower ones up to 20 cm (8 in) long and 15 cm (6 in) wide. The short stemmed flowers stand upright in the forks and at the ends of the branches. The tubular calyx, up to 4.5 cm (1½ in) long, drops after withering to leave ring-shaped calyx base. The funnel-shaped white corolla has a folded five-lobed margin and a corolla tube up to 7.5 cm (3 in) long. The fruit is in an oval capsule up to 5 cm (2 in) long with firm spines on the outside, where four flaps burst open when it is ripening. The fruit contains numerous flat, blackish seeds.
Flowering time: Early summer to mid-autumn or fall.
Habitat: The white thorn apple is not uncommon on rubbish tips, round the edges of fields and in vineyards but it is usually rather erratic.
Distribution: The original home of the thorn apple and the history of its migration into Central and Eastern Europe is not yet clear. It is now found everywhere in temperate and warm zones.
Parts used: Herbage (Herba Stramonii), seeds (Semen Stramonii).
Harvesting time: Herbage early summer to early autumn or fall, seeds early to mid-autumn or fall.
Harvesting instructions: The plant is collected in dry weather and after the thicker parts of the stems have been removed is dried at a temperature of 50 to 60 °C. The drugs are odourless and have a very bitter, salty taste.
Beware! All parts of this plant are poisonous!
Ingredients: The drugs contain 0.2 to 0.6 per cent alkaloids. The principal alkaloid is L-Hyoscyamin, next atropin and L-Scopolamin.
Uses: The effect of the drugs depends on their alkaloid content and is like that of the deadly nightshade (Atropa belladonna). While the seeds are preferred for extraction of the alkaloids, the herbage is used to manufacture asthma-cigarettes or as an asthma fumigant powder. The alkaloids are also used to relieve bronchial cramps.
Toxic effect: Poisoning is not uncommon and generally occurs through mistaken identity or excessive smoking of asthma-cigarettes. The symptoms of poisoning are similar to those of the deadly nightshade (Atropa belladonna).
History: The thorn apple was introduced into Spain from the Americas in 1577 and used as a drug since 1762. The plants described in Fuchs' and Bock's herbals are South Asian and South African kinds of thorn apple.

Thorn Apple

†FOXGLOVE   *Digitalis purpurea* L.

Family: Scrophulariaceae.
Description: This biennial plant has many thin branching roots. In its first year it produces a rosette of petioled, basal leaves, some of which wither the following year when the stem develops 30 to 120 cm (1−4 ft) high. This is simple or forked, slightly leaved and felted with grey hairs. Both sides of the leaves are covered in dense hair. The nodding flowers are borne in a terminal one-sided spike. The corolla develops into a finger-shaped, bell-like, mostly light purple, occasionally white tube. It is covered with upright standing hairs and patterned with dark, lightly-bordered spots.
Flowering time: Summer.
Habitat: This plant thrives particularly on lime-deficient soil containing manganese, from the plains to lower mountain slopes but principally in forest clearings.
Distribution: In Europe the foxglove extends northwards as far as Southern Sweden, in the West from Ireland via Great Britain to Belgium, Holland and France, and in the South-West as far as the Iberian Peninsula. In Germany it is abundant in the lower mountains.
Parts used : Leaves (Folia Digitalis).
Harvesting time: Mid to late summer.
Harvesting instructions: The leaves are collected on sunny afternoons and dried in thin layers. The drug has an unpleasant smell and a sharp offensive bitter taste.
Beware! All parts of the plant are poisonous!
Ingredients: The leaves of the red foxglove contain 0.2−0.6 per cent of cardiotonic glycosides especially the purpurea glycosides A and B that are easily converted by glucose-splitting into secondary glycosides digitoxin and gitoxin. They also contain saponins and flavones.
Uses: The red foxglove and woolly foxglove are among the most important medicinal plants containing cardio-tonic glycosides. The pure glycosides, especially digitoxin (D. purpurea) and digoxin (D. lanata) are exclusively used therapeutically nowadays. Their use depends on strict medical instructions according to the different kinds of heart incompetence.
Toxic effects: Poisoning from the plants themselves is rare because their toxic effect is generally recognised. An overdose lowers the pulse rate, causes nausea, vomiting and uncoordinated contractions of the different parts of the heart leading to cardiac arrest.
History: The application of the drug as an emetic, mentioned by Fuchs and Bock, probably refers to symptoms of poisoning. In 1785 the Scottish Dr Withering stated the correct dosage which is still valid in principle today.

Foxglove

†MALE FERN   *Dryopteris filix-mas (L.) SCHOTT*

Family: Aspidiaceae.

Description: The vigorous unjointed rootstock (rhizome) is about 30 cm (1 ft) long and almost the thickness of a finger, and with the remains of old frond stems can become as thick as a fist. Its 50–100 cm (20–39 in) high bi-pinnate fronds form a funnel. The stems of the fronds and the pinnae themselves are covered in brown scaly hairs. The fronds are quite tough and only destroyed by severe frost. The seed vessels (sori) with their kidney-shaped veils are attached to the underside of the fronds.

Spores mature: Early summer to early autumn.

Habitat: The male fern grows in woods, on the outskirts of woods, in hedges, on stony hillsides and among damp rocks. It is generally widespread from the plains to the alpine regions.

Distribution: The male fern is spread over the whole world, except for the Arctic zone, Africa and Australia.

Parts used: The rootstock (Rhizoma Filicis).

Harvesting time: Early to mid-autumn or fall.

Harvesting instructions: Having dug up the plant, cut off the roots and remove all but the lower 3 cm (1¼ in) of the fronds, as well as any dead parts of the rootstock. The drug should be pre-dried in the open air and then thoroughly dried in heat. It has a nauseating smell and tastes unpleasantly sweet, astringent and irritating.

Ingredients: The effective ingredients of the drug are as follows: the butanonphloroglucides filmaron, filicin, flavaspidin, albaspidin, flavaspid acid, filixic acid and aspidinol, fatty oil, resin.

Uses: Only a few decades ago the male fern counted as the most effective means of combating tapeworms, but the ingredients of the drug are rather toxic and not very stable. For this reason the drug has more recently been superseded by more stable and reliable synthetic preparations.

Toxic effect: Reabsorption of the drug's ingredients through the intestines can cause vomiting, dizziness, stomachache, cramp, circulatory disorders, damaged liver and in rare cases blindness or death through cramps or paralysis of the respiratory system.

History: Theophrastus was the first to mention the drug. While it was rarely used in the Middle Ages, its healing powers were rediscovered in the eighteenth century. The ethereal extract was introduced into treatment in 1835.

Male Fern

HORSETAIL   *Equisetum arvense* L.

Family: Equisetaceae.
Description: The horsetail's rootstock, by means of which it survives the winter, extends over a large area deep in the earth. The shoots, which usually grow afresh each year, emerge from this rootstock. They are already lying under the surface in the autumn and shoot up in the spring. Each of these shoots, which have no chlorophyll, bears a terminal spike consisting of numerous spore capsules. The fertile shoots die soon after the spores ripen. Afterwards the rootstock sends up many infertile, green, verticillate, branched shoots, up to 40 cm (15 in) high.
Spores mature: Early to mid-spring.
Habitat: Horsetail is often found in fields as an almost indestructible weed. It is also found beside paths and in undergrowth and prefers a not too wet loamy or sandy soil. It grows from the lowlands up into the alpine regions (2500 m / 8200 ft).
Distribution: The plant is distributed over the greater part of the Northern Hemisphere. In America it reaches far to the south, beyond the equator.
Parts used: Foliage (Herba Equiseti).
Harvesting time: Early summer to early autumn or fall.
Harvesting instructions: The dried plant is collected without its roots. Any damaged parts are removed. It is dried in thin layers which should be frequently turned. The drug is almost odourless, tastes slightly salty and astringent and crunches when chewed.
Ingredients: The drug contains up to 10 per cent of partly water-soluble silicic acid, saponins, flavonglycosides and nicotine.
Uses: Horsetail is prescribed because of its flavonoid and saponine content as a diuretic for kidney and bladder disorders, cystitis and dropsy. Due to its soluble silicic acid content the drug was once used in the treatment of tuberculosis. It was sometimes used externally to treat slow healing wounds and ulcers, and as a mouth wash and gargle.
Side effects: The drug has no side effects.
History: It is not known definitely if the drug was used in antiquity. In the sixteenth century it was particularly praised for its haemostatic qualities. Kneipp recommended horsetail for disorders of the bladder and haemorrhages.

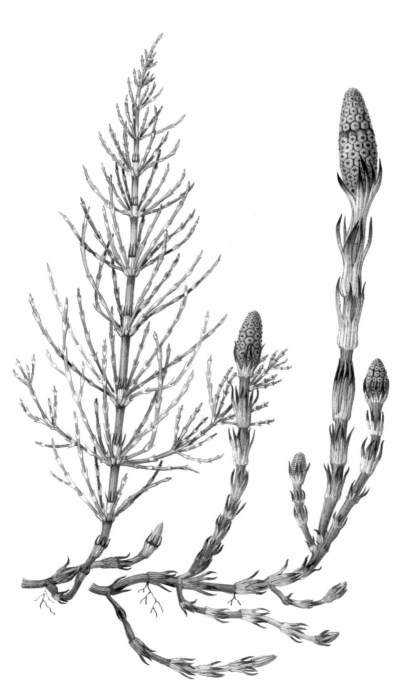

Horsetail

EYEBRIGHT   *Euphrasia officinalis* L.

Family: Scrophulariaceae.

Description: This plant is an annual generally 5−10 cm (2−4 in) high semi-parasite whose host plants are mainly grasses. Eyebright is connected to the roots of its host plant by suction feet. The upright stem is simple or branched and covered in fine hair. All the leaves have short bristly hairs on the underside. The flowers come in terminal spikes on the branches. The corolla is white, occasionally lilac, the upper lip violet and the lower lip marked with a yellow throat and dark lines. The great variability of this species led to the creation of some sub-species.

Flowering time: Late spring to mid-autumn or fall.

Habitat: Eyebright is the most common species of this genus in Germany. It grows in meadows and on heaths and bogland and in light woods, from the lowlands to the mountains.

Distribution: The plant grows over the whole of Central Europe. In the West it is found from France to England, in the North as far as Southern Scandinavia, in the South to Northern Italy and in the East to the northern parts of the Balkan peninsula and Russia.

Parts used: Flowering herbage (Herba Euphrasiae).

Harvesting time: Mid-summer to mid-autumn or fall.

Harvesting instructions: The herbage is gathered without the lower stems and dried, during which it must not discolour. The drug is odourless and has a slightly bitter and weak salty taste.

Ingredients: The plant contains the glycoside aucubin, furthermore some ethereal oil, and bitter constituents, tannin, resin and flavonoids.

Uses: As its name suggests the drug was used particulaly for eye complaints, particularly conjunctivitis and inflammation of the cornea and eyelids and, together with chamomile flowers, for styes. It is also used for eye strain and slackness of the eyelids, and for coughs and sneezes.

Side effects: There are no known side effects.

History: Eyebright was known in antiquity. Dioscorides mentions in his writings that the drug was used as eye drops. The healing effect of the plant was also recognised in the Middle Ages.

Eyebright

BEECH   *Fagus sylvatica* L.

Family: Fagaceae.
Description: Beech forms an upright tree up to 30 m (98 ft) or more high. Its straight trunk is cylindrical, the bark is often encrusted with lichen, particularly on younger trees where it is smooth and silver-grey. Early in the year leaves and flowers emerge together from long-stemmed buds. The reddish-brown bracts drop off early. The inflorescences are borne in the axils of the leaves, the males long-stemmed and deeper than the females. The flowers are contained in a soft bristly brown husk which later becomes a woody, four-part cupule. This generally contains two fruits, which are single-seeded, triangular, red-brown, shiny nuts (beech nuts).
Flowering time: Late spring.
Habitat: Beech is a tree characteristic of the oceanic climate. It grows in the lowlands up to the mountain ranges and alpine foothills (up to 1700 m / 5500 ft) and often forms large areas of unmixed population.
Distribution: Beech trees can be found in most parts of Europe and in the Caucasus. In the north they extend to Bergen (Norway), under the influence of the Gulf Stream, in the east from Southern Sweden via the Vistula estuary and Southern Poland to the Crimea.
Use as medicine: Only beechwood tar (Pix Fagi) is used in medicine. The bark is used for tannin, the leaves as a tobacco substitute and tea, and cooking oil is extracted from the fruits. The residue of the compressed beechnuts contains oxalic acid which causes stomach upsets, sickness and vomiting.
Extraction: Pix Fagi is extracted from beech trunks and branches by dry distillation. Beechwood tar is an oily, black-brown, slightly granular transparent liquid. It has a distinctive burning smell and a repulsive bitter, acrid taste.
Ingredients: Beechwood tar contains phenol, cresole, creosote, guajacol, hydrocarbons, fatty acids and fatty acid esters. After a shake out with soda lye the creosote is extracted by way of distillation.
Uses: Beechwood is used externally for its phenols and hydrocarbons, which have antiseptic and fungicidal effects and reduce itching, for skin complaints like eczema, herpes and scabies. The creosote, whose main constituent is guajacol, is used for bronchial catarrh. Guajacol is an ingredient of cough syrups.
Side effects: Undiluted beechwood tar causes local irritation to skin and mucus membranes which can lead to inflammatory changes when used for a long time.
History: Beech oil was first extracted in England in 1713 and recommended as a replacement for olive oil.

Beech

MEADOWSWEET

Filipendula ulmaria
MAXIM.

Family: Rosaceae.

Description: Meadowsweet is a herbaceous perennial 1 to 1½ m (3−5 ft) high which survives the winter by means of its underground creeping rootstocks. Each year this forms a basal rosette of leaves from which rises an upright, leafy stem, branched only near the top. The pinnate leaves are smooth on top and hairy underneath. The many-flowered inflorescences in umbel-like panicles are borne at the ends of the main and side shoots. The strongly scented flowers have five or six 2 to 5 mm long white petals.

Flowering time: Early to mid-summer.

Habitat: The plant grows on both chalky and non-chalky soils, but prefers soil rich in nutrients. It is found mainly on the banks of flowing and still water, in damp meadows and roadside ditches, and mainly in colonies among reeds and in wooded water meadows.

Distribution: Meadowsweet grows from Great Britain right through Europe and Western Asia to the Altai Mountains and Mongolia. Its northern boundary runs from Iceland via the North Cape to North Siberia. In the south it extends to the Mediterranean, the northern Balkan countries and Asiatic Turkey.

Parts used: Flowers (Flores Spiraeae).

Harvesting time: Late spring to mid-summer.

Harvesting instructions: The flowers are gathered without their stems and dried. The drug smells of bitter almonds and has a slight aromatic and astringent taste.

Ingredients: Main ingredients of the plant are salicylic acid compounds. It contains gaultherin and aglycon salicylic acid methylester, spiraein and its aglycon salicylaldehyde and free salicylic acid, citric acid, furthermore tannin and some ethereal oil.

Uses: The effect of the drug is based on its salicyl acid derivatives so, like willow bark, it is noted as a vegetable salicyl acid preparation. Salicyl acid methylester is prescribed for external use against rheumatism.

Side effects: Salicylic acid methylester is poisonous. But poisoning from the plant is most unlikely because of its low content of effective substances.

History: The drug was developed late as a medicine then replaced by the synthesised salicylic acid (Kolbe 1859). The annual world production of acetylsalicylic acid (aspirin), introduced as an analgesic in 1898, is currently about 3000 tons.

Meadowsweet

FENNEL   *Foeniculum vulgare* MILL.

Family: Umbelliferae.

Description: Fennel is a biennial and perennial plant with a finger-thick, spindle-shaped root. In its second year it produces an upright as high as a man that branches towards the top. The whole plant has a strong spicy smell. The feathery divided leaves on the lower part of the plant are petiolated. The smallish flowers are arranged in 4 to 25 small umbels whose stems (rays) are usually of unequal length to form an umbel up to 15 cm (6 in) across. The stamens with their lemon-yellow anthers overtop the five golden-yellow petals. An eliptical schizocarp arises from the ovary, its partial fruits grooved with oil channels.

Flowering time: Mid-summer to early autumn or fall.

Habitat: The plant is a native only of the Mediterranean area but is cultivated on a large scale as a vegetable, spice and medicinal plant.

Distribution: Fennel is cultivated and grows wild in the Mediterranean area and far as the East Indies. It also grows in Western and Central Europe, Africa, China, Japan, North and South America.

Parts used: Fruits (Fructus Foeniculi).

Harvesting time: Late summer to early autumn or fall.

Harvesting instructions: The central umbels collected in September are richest in useful materials. They are dried in a shady, well ventilated area. The drug has a pleasant spicy fragrance and an initially sweet but later burning taste.

Ingredients: Fennel fruits contain, as effective substances, approximately 2.5−6 per cent ethereal oil with anethol and as characteristic constituents, the bitter and camphor-like tasting fenchon, pines, methylchavicol, limones and foeniculin.

Uses: Fennel is used particularly in child care as a phlegm-loosening and expectorant agent in fennel syrup and fennel honey. The drug excites the glistening epithelium of the respiratory tract and is prescribed for coughs, bronchitis and asthma. It stimulates the appetite, is a digestant, sedative and carminative and is used for indigestion and kidney stones. The ethereal oil has an exciting effect on the intestinal muscles, is added to laxatives and counteracts slack intestines. Fennel is also a galactogogue and was in the past prescribed for external use against conjunctivitis and served as a spice. The drug is also used in the liquor industry.

Side effects: Large doses of fennel oil cause excitement of the central nervous system.

History: Fennel was used by the Egyptians and Greeks. Charlemagne ordered its cultivation in 812. First reports of the extraction of fennel oil by water distillation appeared in 1500. The oil was listed in the medical supply list of the city of Berlin in 1574.

Fennel

WILD STRAWBERRY   *Fragaria vesca* L.

Family: Rosaceae.
Description: The wild strawberry survives the winter by means of its short rootstock (rhizome) which is covered in the remains of the dead leaves. Creeping runners that root from the nodes emerge from the axils of the basal leaves. The leaves are tripartite and the small individual leaflets are coarsely serrated. The flowers stand in few-flowered cymes on long pedicels. Besides the five green sepals, there is a ring of five small green leaflets (the outer calyx) outside the calyx. The flowers have five white petals and about 20 stamens. When the fruit ripens the domed base of the flower develops into a juicy aromatic red strawberry. This is a false fruit because the true fruits are arranged over its surface as tiny achenes.
Flowering time: Late spring to early summer.
Habitat: The wild strawberry grows on all types of soil from the lowlands up to the upper tree limit. It prefers light places on nutritious soil in deciduous and coniferous woodland, hedges and the outskirts of woods.
Distribution: The wild strawberry grows in practically the whole of Europe and in the larger part of temperate Asia as far as the Lake Baikal. The plant was probably imported to many parts of the world by settlers.
Parts used: Leaves (Folia Fragariae).
Harvesting time: Late spring to early summer.
Harvesting instructions: The leaves with their stems are picked and spread out in a thin layer in a shady well ventilated place. Discoloured material is removed during the drying process. The drug is odourless with a slightly astringent taste.
Ingredients: The strawberry leaves contain tannin, vitamin C, flavonoids, ethereal oil and silicic acid.
Uses: The drug is effective because of its tannin content, which has an astringent effect, the reason for its use in treating diarrhoea. The younger leaves serve as a black tea substitute.
Side effects: There are no known side effects.
History: The strawberry is mentioned in the oldest records and there are many descriptions of its fruit. Achenes from the fruit have been found dating from the lake-dwelling era. Abbess Hildegard of Bingen mentions the strawberry in her writings.

116

Wild Strawberry

ALDER BUCKTHORN   *Frangula alnus* MILL.

Family: Rhamnaceae.

Description: The alder buckthorn is generally a 2½ to 3½ m (8–11½ ft) high shrub, occasionally a small tree. The young bark is green or dark and later becomes grey-brown with the characteristic light, long, lenticels. The thin-skinned leaves vary greatly in size and shape, but are always covered in hair when young. The five-lobed greenish white pedicellated flowers are borne in 2 to 10 flowered cymes in the leaf axils. The fruit, a berry-like two or three seeded drupe, is at first green, but later red and then black when ripe.

Flowering time: Late spring to early summer.

Habitat: The alder buckthorn grows in the lowlands right up into the foothills of the mountains on bare, sunny slopes, in thickets, light woods, beside watercourses and on bogland. It grows up to the 1000 m (3300 ft) contour in the Alps.

Distribution: This shrub is a native of most of Europe, extending in the north to Central Norway and Sweden, southwards to Central Spain, Italy and Northern Greece and further east via Asia Minor to the Caucasus. It can also be found in North America.

Parts used: Bark (Cortex Frangulae).

Harvesting time: Mid-spring to early summer.

Harvesting instructions: The side branches are cut from the shrub and circular incisions are made, linked by longitudinal cuts, then the bark is peeled off. It can be dried in the sun but can only be used medicinally after it has been stored for a year. The drug has a putrid smell and a bitter, repulsive taste.

Ingredients: The fresh alder buckthorn rind contains anthron and anthronol derivates which cause nausea. When stored for long periods or when the drug is heated the oxidation converts it into anthrachinon derivates which have a laxative effect, such as glucofrangulin A and B which are easily converted into frangulin by splitting the glucose. By way of hydrolysis one obtains emodin and rhamnose. The drug also contains tannin.

Uses: Preparations of the drug are only effective on the large intestines after hours of direct stimulation which triggers off reflex evacuation contractions. Stored alder buckthorn bark has a mild action without side effects and is prescribed for chronic constipation and pregnancy. It is also used for gall-bladder and stomach complaints.

Side effects: The tannin content can cause stomach irritations. Constant use can cause muscle paralysis due to reduced reabsorption of potassium.

History: The drug has been used as a laxative since the fourteenth century.

Alder Buckthorn

COMMON FUMITORY   *Fumaria officinalis* L.

Family: Fumariaceae.

Description: This generally 10 to 30 cm (4−12 in) high annual, blue-green, pruinose plant has one or several stems. The slightly grooved stem is upright or climbing and bears alternate leaves. The tender, petiolated leaves have doubly pinnate blades. The flowers are arranged in several upright, many-flowered, clusters standing above the leaves. The two outer petals are purple-red, and the tips dark red to black, but the uppermost has a short blunt spur, while the two identical-shaped inner petals grow together at the top where like the outer petals, they are dark red to black. Common fumitory can easily be differentiated from other types of fumitory by its sepals which are smaller than the corolla and without its spurs only a third of the length.

Flowering time: Mid-spring to mid-autumn or fall.

Habitat: The common fumitory is a typical plant of cultivated ground and is often found in fields, gardens, on rubbish tips and walls, by roadsides and in vineyards.

Distribution: Apart from the Arctic areas this plant, which originated in the Mediterranean area, can be found throughout Europe, in Western and temperate Asia and North Africa. From here it was distributed by man all over the world.

Parts used: Herbage (Herba Fumariae).

Harvesting time: Late spring to late summer.

Harvesting instructions: The plant is harvested while in flower and dried. It is almost odourless and has an unpleasant bitter, slightly salty taste.

Ingredients: The drug contains the alkaloids fumarin (protopin), cryptocavin, aurotensin, stylopin, sinactin, also fumaric acid, resin, mucilage and bitter constituents.

Uses: Because of its alkaloid content common fumitory has a gall-bladder regulating effect i.e. it reduces excessive gall-bladder secretion and promotes deficient gall-bladder secretion.

Side effects: Poisoning by this plant is unknown.

History: It is not certain if the drug was used in medicine during antiquity. However, it is assumed that Galen used the plant. The drug was in use in the Middle Ages.

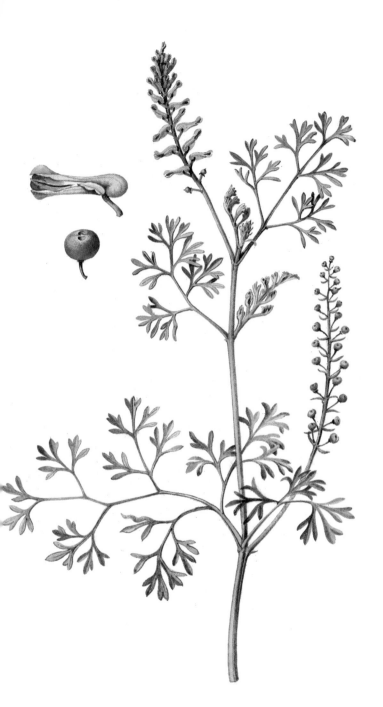

Common Fumitory

GOAT'S RUE   *Galega officinalis* L.

Family: Leguminosae.
Description: Goat's rue is a strong vigorous green herbaceous perennial with numerous upright 40 to 100 cm (15—39 in) high, branched stems. The multi-headed rootstock has fibres and, when the plant is fully grown, bears many upright stems. The short petiolated leaves are imparipinnate. The flower clusters with long pedicels arising from the leaf axils are often taller than the sub-tending leaves. They consist of many slightly nodding bluish white flowers about 1 cm long. The petals have a short claw. The standard petal is as long as the keel.
Flowering time: Mid to late summer.
Habitat: The plant grows on marshy meadows, on banks and in ditches.
Distribution: Goat's rue is a native of Italy, the Balkan and Danube countries and also the Volga. Northwards its distribution extends to the Carpathian and Sudenten Mountains., to the east across Southern Poland to Central Russia, then to the Caucusus and via Turkey to Iraq and Iran. It is assumed that it was introduced into the Iberian Peninsula and Southern France. Goat's rue has been cultivated so long that it is not possible to determine the original limits of its distribution with any certainty.
Parts used: Flowering herbage (Herba Galegae).
Harvesting time: Mid to late summer.
Harvesting instructions: The aerial parts of the plant should be gathered and dried in a warm, well ventilated place. The odourless drug has a bitter, slightly harsh and astringent taste. When the foliage is chewed the saliva turns yellowish green.
Ingredients: The herbage of the goat's rue contains galegin, saponins, tannin and bitter constituents, luteolin and galuteolin.
Uses: The guanidin derivate galegin has blood sugar reducing characteristics probably by having an effect via the vegetative nervous system on the endocrine effective part of the pancreas, the islet of Langerhans. It is dangerous to use, not only because of the poison but also because of its uncertain effect, unlike insulin.
Side effects: Toxic doses of the plant can lead to cramp and eventually death in cattle. Infusions of glucose are ineffective.
History: The drug has been used since the sixteenth century.

Goat's Rue

DOWNY HEMP-NETTLE
Galeopsis segetum NECKER

Family: Labiatae.

Description: The plant's annual taproot produces an upright, branched stem about 50 cm (20 in) high with short fluffy hairs, which is not swollen at the nodes. The lower part of the stem is often tinted red and, like the leaves and calyx, is covered in silky down. There are up to four verticillasters one above the other, usually with four to eight blossoms apiece. The usually sulpher-yellow and slightly downy corolla protrudes a long way from the calyx. The upper lip of the blossom is finely toothed in the middle. The turned down lower lip has a strong yellow spot on the throat, often with a reddish violet pattern on it. The hollow tooth-shaped tubercles at the base of the lower lip are characteristic.

Flowering time: Mid to late summer.

Habitat: The downy hemp-nettle is one of the few purely Atlantic, strictly lime-hating labiates. It is found on sand, gravel, rubble and arable fields, in copses, on the edges of footpaths and in quarries.

Distribution: This plant is fairly widely distributed in Atlantic Euorpe and less frequently found towards the east. It is quite often found in West Germany, especially in sandy areas, in Holstein, Lower Saxony and the Black Forest. Eastwards its distribution extends almost to the Frankish coloured sandstone district in Thuringia.

Parts used: Herbage (Herba Galeopsidis).

Harvesting time: Mid to late summer.

Harvesting instructions: The aerial parts of the plant are collected while it is in flower and dried in a shady, airy place. The drug has a weak, indistinct smell and a bitter, weak, salty, slimy taste.

Ingredients: The downy hemp-nettle plant contains up to 0.9 per cent silicic acid of which up to 0.2 per cent is water soluble. Further constituents are 5 to 10 per cent tannin, a glycosidical bitter principle, saponins, ethereal oil and stachydrin.

Uses: The drug is effective as an astringent medium due to its tannin content. Its saponine content makes it a discharging agent and diuretic. Because of its silicic acid content it was used in the past to help in the treatment of tuberculosis of the lungs.

Side effects: No side effects are known.

History: It is assumed that downy hemp-nettle was used in ancient medicine for lung diseases. The first authentic report in which its use for consumption was reported dates from the year 1792. At the beginning of the nineteenth century the drug was sold at inflated prices as "Lieber's consumption herb" as a nostrum for tuberculosis of the lungs. Entering the plant in the Austrian pharmacopoeia put an end to this.

Downy Hemp-nettle

SWEET WOODRUFF
Galium odoratum (L.) SCOP.

Family: Rubiaceae.

Description: This plant, which grows up to 60 cm (2 ft) high, survives from year to year by means of its thin cylindrical creeping rootstock. In the spring this produces a verticillate-leaved square stem. Each whorl of leaves consists of six to nine leaflets. The much-branched umbel-like inflorescences are borne at the ends of the stems. The pedicellate flowers stand in the axils of tiny bracts, their calyces being almost completely rolled back. The corolla forms a small white tube. The ovary is epigynous and when ripe disintegrates into two single-seeded partial fruits, thickly covered with tiny hooked bristles. These readily cling to people and animals, so they get widely distributed. The whole plant has a pleasant smell, particularly when it withers, by which it can be distinguished from other similar plants.

Flowering time: Late spring to very early summer.

Habitat: This plant prefers to grow in light woodland. It is a typical companion plant of beech trees, but is also found in light coniferous woodland. It likes damp, not too shady places.

Distribution: Sweet Woodruff is a native of Northern and Central Europe as far as the northern Balkan Peninsula. From here its distribution extends to Siberia and over the Italian mountains to North Africa.

Parts used: Herbage (Herba Asperulae).

Harvesting time: Mid-spring to early summer.

Harvesting instructions: The drug is collected shortly before or during flowering time and dried. The fresh plant is odourless, but when dried it smells spicy, rather bitter and astringent.

Ingredients: Sweet woodruff contains the glycoside asperulosid, tannin and bitter constituents, as well as cumarin, which is formed from a glycosidal first stage when the plant withers, giving it the characteristic cumarin smell.

Uses: The ingredients of sweet woodruff are anti-spasmodic, soothing, dilate the peripheral blood vessels, counteract oedema and are anti-inflammatory. The drug was earlier used for gall-stones and gall-bladder illnesses, as well as externally in compresses. Due to its relatively high toxicity the drug is no longer used therapeutically.

Side effects: If used in large doses, cumarin causes stupefaction and violent headaches. This can also be caused by the smell of strong-scented hay. Internal use is likely to damage the liver.

History: The drug and its healing effects were first mentioned in the late Middle Ages. During the period when witches and superstition were rife, it was used to ward off evil spirits.

Sweet Woodruff

*GREAT YELLOW GENTIAN   *Gentiana lutea* L.

Family: Gentianaceae.

Description: The great yellow gentian is an impressive perennial plant some 50 to 140 cm (20−55 in) high. Its multi-headed, little-branched taproot can become as thick as one's arm. The upright, finger-thick cylindrical stem has no branches and the upper part is grooved. The bluish-green leaves are about 30 cm (12 in) long and 15 cm (6 in) wide. They are borne in opposite pairs forming a cross shape and on the upper part of the plant change into saucer-shaped subtending leaves, from the axils of which develop cymes of 3 to 10 long-stemmed flowers. The pale yellow calyx is split on one side. The wheel-shaped corolla is a shining golden-yellow, its tips finally spreading out like a star. The fruit is a pointed, conical capsule, up to 6 cm (2½ in) long, containing many seeds.

Flowering time: Summer.

Habitat: The great yellow gentian normally grows in groups and prefers chalky soil. It likes the light undergrowth on shaded mountain slopes or rubbish tips and poor pastures.

Distribution: The plant is distributed throughout the Southern European mountain ranges (up to 2500 m (8200 ft) and occasionally found in the lower mountain ranges from the Pyrenean peninsula to Turkey.

Parts used: Root (Radix Gentianae).

Harvesting time: Early to mid-autumn or fall.

Harvesting instructions: The taproots are dug out, washed well and dried in artificial heat. The drug consists mainly of the roots of Gentiana lutea but also other types of gentian. It has a weak sweet spicy smell and tastes sweet at first, but later very bitter.

Ingredients: The main ingredients of the drug are the bitter constituents amarogentin (0.04 per cent − bitter value 58,000 000) and gentiopicrosid (4.5 per cent − bitter value 12,000), fermentable sugar, pectin.

Uses: Taken half an hour before mealtimes the drug's bitter constituents stimulate the secretions in the gastro-intestinal tract and are prescribed as an aperitif in cases of indigestion. The stomach then enjoys a better blood supply, is more rapidly emptied and the nutrients are quite easily reabsorbed, so the drug acts as a restorative. The fermented drug is used in the liquor industry (gentian schnaps).

Side effects: Using larger doses of the drug can cause stomach upsets and eventually vomiting. Poisoning is unknown.

History: Dioscorides and Pliny mention this gentian and report that it was named after Prince Genthius. They used the root as a bitter constituent.

Great Yellow Gentian

HERB ROBERT — *Geranium robertianum* L.

Family: Geraniaceae.

Description: Herb robert is an annual or perennial plant with a weak, branched taproot that first forms a rosette of leaves. After the stem has grown up these leaves soon dry up. The 20−60 cm (8−24 in) long, squarrose, sparsely branched stems with numerous glandular hairs vary from prostrate to upright and, like the leaves, are often a brilliant carmine-red. The axis of the inflorescence springs from the axils of the leaves which each bear four small bracts and two pedicellated flowers. The petals are light to bright red, often with three lighter longitudinal stripes. The whole plant has an unpleasant smell.

Flowering time: Late spring to mid-autumn or fall.

Habitat: Herb robert inhabits mainly shady, damp, nutrient-rich soils in our deciduous and mixed forests, but also grows in sunny dry places.

Distribution: The plant is a native of most of Europe (apart from its most northerly areas). From here it reaches eastwards to Japan and southwards to Central Africa. In America it appears to be a native only of Atlantic North America.

Parts used: Flowering herbage (Herba Ruperti).

Harvesting time: Late spring to mid-autumn or fall.

Harvesting instructions: The flowering herbage is gathered without its seeds during dry weather and dried. Fresh herb robert has an astringent taste and a repulsive smell which completely disappears when it is dried.

Ingredients: The drug mainly contains tannin, malic and citric acid.

Uses: Herb robert was once used as an astringent because of its tannin content.

Side effects: It has no known side effects.

History: The drug was used throughout the Middle Ages as a healing plant for many complaints. Paracelsus recommended that the dried and powdered herbage should be sprinkled on bread. According to him the powder should strengthen the heart and lift depression.

Herb Robert

GROUND IVY   *Glechoma hederacea* L.

Family: Labiatae.
Description: Ground ivy is a perennial, herbaceous plant with a spicy smell. It has a creeping main shoot that bears leaves even in winter and whose lower nodes have roots. The 20—40 cm (8—15 in) long shoots develop at the front of the plant. The leaves are often suffused red-violet beneath. After flowering the plant grows many leaf runners up to 1 m (3 ft) long. The clearly pedicellated flowers are mostly borne in twos or threes in the axils of the leaves. The flower's bilabiate character is clearly visible from the five petals united into a straight tube forming a blue-violet corolla.
Flowering time: Mid-spring to early summer.
Habitat: Due to its runners the ground ivy can be found in extensive colonies in fallow fields and meadows, under bushes and trees, in hedgerows and deciduous woods, mainly in moist, rich soil.
Distribution: Ground ivy is a native of most of Europe and temperate regions of Asia as far as Japan. In Europe its habitat stretches from the Mediterranean to the northern parts of Scandinavia. It has become a native of America since it was colonised.
Parts used: Herbage (Herba Glechomae).
Harvesting time: Mid-spring to early summer.
Harvesting instructions: The aerial parts of the plant are gathered while in flower and dried in a shady, protected place. Fresh or dried, the drug has a spicy aromatic smell and a spicy, bitter, harsh taste which leaves an irritating feeling.
Ingredients: The ground ivy contains 0.03—0.06 per cent ethereal oil, 3—7 per cent tannin, and the bitter constituents glecomin, saponin, resin and wax.
Uses: Its relatively high tannin content explains why the drug is used for diarrhoea.
Side effects: The plant's poisonous effect is attributable to its glechomin, which can be fatal, particularly for horses.
History: Ground ivy is an old healing plant which also played a role in superstition and witchcraft in the Middle Ages.

Ground Ivy

†HEDGE HYSSOP   *Gratiola officinalis* L.

Family: Scrophulariaceae.
Description: This plant survives from year to year by means of its creeping, jointed rootstock. The upright hollow stem, about 15–30 cm (6–12 in) high, is simple or sparsely branched. The bases of its up to 5 cm (2 in) long opposite leaves, arranged in a cruciform pattern, clasp half way round the stem. The 8–10 mm long bilabiate corolla is white to reddish tinted and reddish veined. Its wide tube, covered with hair inside, ends in a five-part fringe with flat lobes, of which the two flat round ones form the upper lip and the three more deeply incised ones the lower lip.
Flowering time: Summer.
Habitat: The plant is fairly widespread in damp areas as well as wet places and ditches, in pools and on marshy meadows. It is missing from some areas such as the higher alpine valleys and is mainly found in the lowlands.
Distribution: Hedge hyssop is a native of Central and Southern Europe across to Western and Northern Asia and also North America.
Parts used: Herbage (Herba Gratiolae).
Harvesting time: Summer.
Harvesting instructions: The aerial parts of the plant are gathered while it is in flower and dried in a shady, well ventilated area. The drug is almost odourless and has a very bitter, burning taste. Beware! This plant is poisonous!
Ingredients: The drug contains the glycoside gratiosid (gratiolin) and gratiotoxin, the triterpenderivate gratiolon, resin, tannin acid and ethereal oil.
Uses: The locally irritating effect of the drug is attributed to the gratiosid. The gratiotoxin has a digitalis-like effect. The drug was previously used as a drastic laxative, as a diuretic for gout as well as for chronic dermatitis. The plant is no longer used.
Toxic effect: The constituents of the drug cause, with higher doses, bloody diarrhoea, abortion, violent vomiting, cramp, heart disorders and breathing paralysis with fatal consequences, particularly with abortions.
History: During the Middle Ages the drug was a highly valued medicine listed in all the herbals.

Hedge Hyssop

STRAW FLOWER
Helichrysum arenarium (L.) MOENCH

Family: Compositae.

Description: This plant, about 10 to 30 cm (4−12 in)high, survives by means of its spindle-shaped, several-headed woody root, which in springtime puts forth flowerless shoots and plain leafy pedicels. About three to 20 flowers appear in tight terminal clusters. The small spherical flower heads are surrounded by a sheath of many scales (squama), regular in formation, with a dry skin and lemon-yellow to orange, occasionally white in colour. The fruits have a hairy pappus to facilitate distribution. When crushed the flowers give off an aromatic scent.

Flowering time: Summer.

Habitat: The helichrysum is found in abundance almost exclusively in the plains on sandy soil, containing little lime, and also to some extent where there is gypsum or dolomite in the soil, as on sandy hillsides, in sandy grassland and dunes, as well as in dry pine forests.

Distribution: In Central Europe this plant is found from North Baden and the Rhineland westwards to Holland and Belgium. Its northern limit extends through Denmark. Further east it appears only as far as the northern and central parts of the Soviet Union and the Caucasus. In the south-east it is met as far as the Central Balkans.

Parts used: Heads of blossom (Flores Stoechados).

Harvesting time: Summer.

Harvesting instructions: The clusters of flowers are plucked off before they are in full bloom by holding the stem firmly with one hand. The yellow colour of the flowerheads must be preserved when they are dried. The drug smells slightly aromatic and tastes bitter and spicy.

Ingredients: The flowerheads of the helichrysum arenarium contain isosalipuroside, flavonglycoside of naringenin, camphor and apigenin, phthalide as well as the arenarin complex which acts as an antibiotic.

Uses: By reason of its flavonglycoside content the drug has a diuretic effect and promotes the discharge of bile and was earlier used in cases of chronic inflammation of the gall-bladder. It also stimulates the secretion of gastric and pancreatic juices and promotes the appetite. It is said to be effective against moths and is used for decorating blends of tea.

Toxic effect: The non-toxic arenarin promotes plant growth and increases the yield of fruits.

History: Species of helichrysum were used in ancient times and the Middle Ages as herbal cures for dysentery.

Straw Flower

†BLACK HELLEBORE   *Helleborus niger* L.

Family: Ranunculaceae.

Description: The black hellebore (Christmas rose) is a perennial plant up to 35 cm (14 in) high. It overwinters by means of its short, blackish-brown rootstock and puts forth one or more stems. The overwintering leaves at ground level are leathery and generally a glossy dark green. Usually one bloom is carried on each thick upright pedicel. The blooms at the end of these pedicels grow to about 7 cm (3 in) across. The petals are like the sepals of most flowering plants and white or pale pink at first, later turning green or crimson. The similar green hellebore (Helleborus viridis L.) has grass-green blossoms.

Flowering time: January to April, sometimes as early as December.

Habitat: The black hellebore is a plant of mountain regions, prefers open woodland or copses and colonises chalky soils almost exclusively. It is also a popular garden plant.

Distribution: The main centre of its distribution lies in the Alps. From here the distribution of the green hellebore extends to North-West France, into southern Central Europe and to Hungary, while the black hellebore is found only in the Apennines and Carpathian mountains. In northern Central Europe both species are only found as garden escapes.

Parts used: Rhizome (Rhizoma Hellebori nigri).

Harvesting time: Early spring.

Harvesting instructions: The rootstock is cleaned of any remaining soil, thick pieces are split longitudinally, then dried on a line. The drug has a mildly offensive smell and tastes sweet at first, later sharp and caustic.

Beware! All parts of this plant are poisonous!

Ingredients: The drug contains the bitter-tasting glycoside hellebrin, the saponin helleborin, aconite acid and traces of ethereal oils, but in contrast with the green hellebore, no alkaloids.

Uses: Preparations of the root were used in cases of weak heart, and as a diuretic. The helleborin causes the drug's emetic, drastic purgative and narcotic effects.

Toxic effect: Reabsorption of large doses of substances contained in the drug causes excitement and then paralysis of the central nervous system.

History: Theophrastus and Dioscorides refer to the plant's toxicity, which was also mentioned, with reference to its healing powers in mediaeval herbals.

Black Hellebore

RUPTURE WORT   *Herniaria glabra* L.

Family: Caryophyllaceae.

Description: Glabrous rupture wort is an insignificant plant which lies flat on the ground. It grows numerous many-branched stems up to 30 cm (1 ft) long, that creap over the ground, often forming a dense carpet. The tiny flowers are quinate. Their clustered inflorescences each consist of ten flowers. The sepals overtop all the other parts of the flower, even the five inconspicuous white petals. Hairy rupture wort (Herniaria hirsuta), also used as a drug, differs from glabrous rupture wort mainly by its extremely hairy leaves.

Flowering time: Mid-summer to early autumn or fall.

Habitat: Both species are often found on dry sandy soils, heath-land, beside footpaths and on the dry surface of alluvial sands on riverbanks, but are often overlooked because of their unobtrusive appearance.

Distribution: Both species are natives of Central and Southern Europe, North Africa and temperate Asia as far as Siberia. The glabrous rupture wort can be found as far north as Scotland and Scandinavia, the hairy wort on the other hand, apart from North Africa, in Ethiopia, the Cape and in the Canary Islands.

Parts used: Herbage (Herba Herniariae).

Harvesting time: Mid-summer to early autumn or fall.

Harvesting instructions: The aerial parts of the plant are gathered in late afternoon while in flower and dried in the shade. The drug has a pleasant cumarin-like smell and a slightly scratchy taste.

Ingredients: The drug mainly contains the oxycumarins umbellife-ron and herniarin, saponins, flavonglycosides, tannin and approximately 0.6 per cent ethereal oil.

Uses: Glabrous rupture wort has a slight antispasmodic, astringent and disinfecting effect on the urinary passage and was therefore used for bladder complaints.

Side effects: No side effects are known.

History: The drug played no part in medicine in antiquity and during the Middle Ages. Its use in folk medicine for hernias is noteworthy and must be attributed to the signature teachings of Paracelsus.

Rupture Wort

HOP   *Humulus lupulus* L.

Family: Urticaceae.

Description: The hop is a 3 to 6 m (10−20 ft) long perennial, herbaceous climbing plant that overwinters by means of its strong, branched root. The stems, as thick as a quill, twine clockwise and carry many small climbing tendrils. The leaves are long petiolated and usually ternate or quinate. The flowers of the dioecious plants are borne in inflorescences − the male in paniculate cymes, the females in dense-flowered cymose spikes. The flowers later become enlarged into oval 'cones' (strobiles). The yellow-green, later yellow-brown fruit scales have resin glands at the base, the ovary develops into a light-coloured nut up to 6 mm long. Numerous types were bred for cultivation.

Flowering time: Mid to late summer.

Habitat: The hop is a plant of damp places. It is found on hedges and fences, the outskirts of woods and meadow copses. Because of the aromatic taste of the female inflorescence (hop cones) and its use in breweries, hops (always female plants) have been cultivated in many parts of Central Europe since the eighth century.

Distribution: Hops are found in temperate zones of Eurasia and the Americas.

Parts used: Fruits (Fructus Humuli).

Harvesting time: Late summer to early autumn or fall.

Harvesting instructions: The female cones are gathered as they start to ripen and are not yet brown and dried at 40 to 50°C. This opens up the inflorescence and the hop glands (Glandulae Lupuli), which secrete the sticky yellow hop flour (Lupulin), drop out. The drug has an aromatic smell and a spicy, slightly bitter taste.

Ingredients: Hop fruits contain 15 to 30 per cent resin and approximately 0.14 per cent ethereal oil, the glands approximately 80 per cent resin and 1 to 3 per cent ethereal oil. The main constituents of the resin fraction, accounting for 50 per cent, are the alpha-hop bitter acids humulon, cohumulon and adhumulon and also the beta-hop bitter acid lupulon; furthermore it contains approximately 10 per cent xanthohumol.

Uses: Hop bitters have a calming, antibiotic and oestrogen effect. The drug is a mild soporific and sedative for nervous stomach complaints, sexual excitement and sometimes as a diuretic. The active ingredients serve as an aromatic flavouring and preservative for beer.

Side effects: Fresh hop fruits can cause hypersomnia and vomiting, profuse perspiration and a state of excitement, and particularly dermatitis (hop picker's disease).

History: The drug has been used for about 200 years.

Hop

†HENBANE   *Hyoscyamus niger* L.

Family: Solanaceae.

Description: A 20−80 cm (8−32 in) high stem rises from the henbane's annual or biennial branched root, which, like the foliage and calyx, is tufted with sticky hairs. The individual flowers carried close to the leaf axils form a long one-sided spike. The urn-shaped calyx is split into five apiculate teeth. The bell-shaped, five-lobed, dirty yellow corolla, whose throat is usually red-violet, is covered with a network of dark violet veins. The anthers are violet.

Flowering time: Early summer to mid-autumn or fall.

Habitat: Henbane often appears scattered on rubbish tips, footpaths and at the side of village roads.

Distribution: Henbane originated in the Mediterranean area and the arid regions of Central and East Asia. In Central Europe it is spread from the plains up into the alpine foothills. It is widely distributed in Europe, reaching latitude 63° N, and in the east to Northern and Western Asia and India and in the south to North Africa. It has also colonised parts of East Asia, North America and Australia.

Parts used: Herbage (Herba Hyoscyami).

Harvesting time: Mid-summer.

Harvesting instructions: The drug is collected while in flower after several dry days. The older parts of the stem are removed and it is quickly dried in temperatures up to 60°C. When fresh it has a strong narcotic smell; dried it is almost odourless and has a bitter and sharp taste.

Beware! The drug is very poisonous!

Ingredients: The henbane contains 0.03−0.17 per cent alkaloids. Main alkaloids are L-hyoscyamin and L-scopolamin, secondary alkaloids are racemat (atropin or atroscin) as well as cuskhygrin, choline and tannin.

Uses: Because of their L-hyoscyamin or atropin content drug extracts have the following effects like those of belladonna preparations: pupil-dilatory, anticonvulsive, astringent and anti-emetic and in small doses it has a stimulating effect and in large doses a paralysing effect on the central nervous system. L-scopolamin (hyoscin) has the same characteristics, but only a dampening effect on the cerebrum and is prescribed for states of excitement and to create twilight sleep for the mentally ill. The main use for compound preparations of medical specialities containing alkaloids is for cramp of the smooth muscles in the digestive, urinary and breathing tracts.

Toxic effect: It can produce dilation of the pupils, excitement, confusion and long deep sleep. A 5 mg dose of alkaloids is fatal.

History: Henbane was used in antiquity, played an important part in superstition and witchcraft in the Middle Ages and was also used as a narcotic.

Henbane

ST JOHN'S WORT   *Hypericum perforatum* L.

Family: Hypericaceae.

Description: The perforate St John's wort overwinters by means of its wide-spreading rootstock from which, especially from vigorous plants, a large upright tuft of growth appears in spring, usually with 40−50 cm (15−20 in) high angular stems. The opposite leaves are marked with transparent spots formed by the oil cells present in the leaf tissues. The flowers are borne in apical, paniculate inflorescences and each has five free golden-yellow petals. The ovary develops into a dehiscent capsule with three flaps. This St John's wort can easily be differentiated from other related species by its smooth stem with two lengthwise ridges and its entire or only slightly toothed calyx leaves.

Flowering time: Mid to late summer.

Habitat: The plant prefers to colonise dry soils in light woods, meadows and pastures, on heathland, but particularly rail embankments, by footpaths and on fallow land.

Distribution: This St John's wort is widespread in Europe, in the north as far as Central Scandinavia and the Karelian Peninsula, in the east to the Altai Mountains and China, in the south to North Africa. It was introduced to Australia, North and South America.

Parts used: Herbage (Herba Hyperici).

Harvesting time: Mid to late summer.

Harvesting instructions: The herbage is cut off when the plant starts to flower and after bundling is threaded on a string to dry. The drug has a weak aromatic smell and a bitter, slightly astringent taste.

Ingredients: Perforate St John's wort contains up to 1 per cent ethereal oil, approximately 10 per cent catechin tannin, the flavonolglycoside hyperosid, rutin and quercitrin and approximately 0.1 per cent of the red fluorescent colouring hypericin and pseudohypericin.

Uses: The drug is claimed to have a vulnerary and anti-inflammatory effect. It is also used as a diuretic and choleretic as well as for depression ("arnica of the nerves"). These effects are attributed to the hypericin in particular.

Side effects: Hypericin develops toxic substances under the influence of light which act on the skin causing solar dermatitis in human beings and albinos. It can produce blisters and a drop in temperature. Death has only been observed in mice.

History: The plant was mentioned by Dioscorides and in medieval herbals. The colour separation and the appearance of the leaves explain its role in superstition.

St John's Wort

HYSSOP   *Hyssopus officinalis* L.

Family: Labiatae.

Description: This 20 to 60 cm (8−24 in) high sub-shrub produces several upright or ascending more or less branching stems from its vertical taproot. These are woody at the base and covered in loose dull brown bark. Numerous sunken glandular scales release a sharp aromatic smell when the plant is rubbed. From the nodes longer branches or short shoots emerge, and so the foliage here appears to be arranged in whorls. The three to seven flowers are grouped close together in their leaf axils. Several pseudo-whorls are arranged one above the other to from a spike-like inflorescence up to 10 cm (4 in) long. The corolla, usually violet or blue, rarely pink or white, forms a tube, beyond which the four stamens extend quite a long way.

Flowering time: Mid-summer to mid-autumn or fall.

Habitat: Hyssop is usually found in colonies on dry, sunny rock and gravel slopes. In Central Europe it used to be widely cultivated and has become established in some favourable spots, such as the upper and middle Rhine and Neckar valleys.

Distribution: Hyssop is found from the Altai Mountains and Southern Siberia, through the countries around the Caspian and Black Seas, via Bulgaria, Yugoslavia and Southern France to Spain. In Algeria, as in Central Europe (where it extends as far as Southern Norway) it is only found as a remnant of earlier cultivation.

Parts used: Herb (Herba Hyssopi).

Harvesting time: Mid to late summer.

Harvesting instructions: The aerial parts of the plant are collected and dried. The drug has an aromatic smell, like camphor and a sharp, bitter taste.

Ingredients: The hyssop herb contains 0.3−1 per cent ethereal oil, 5−8 per cent tannin, the flavonoid glycosides hesperidin and diosmin, the bitter principle marubiin, resin, sugar and gum.

Uses: Hyssop has similar healing properties to sage. The drug is used externally as a gargle for throat inflammations and hoarseness, and internally for chronic bronchitis and bronchial asthma. The plant is also used as a spice and in producing herb liqueurs.

Side effects: Large doses of hyssop oil act as a spasmodic.

History: Hyssop was introduced from the Mediterranean to Central Europe by the Benedictines in the ninth and tenth centuries and was cultivated in monastery gardens. The hyssop mentioned by Dioscorides as a medicinal herb is probably a kind of wild marjoram. Even the hyssop of the Bible is not identical to our plant. The ethereal oil was included in the Berlin apothecary's list as early as 1574.

Hyssop

ELECAMPANE
Inula helenium L.

Family: Compositae.

Description: Elecampane is a tall perennial plant that survives the winter by means of its robust rootstock. This root develops some basal leaves followed by a 50−150 cm (20−60 in) high vertical stem, which is covered in matted hair, and can be branched at the top. The large, alternately arranged leaves are covered beneath with thick grey felted hair. The 6−7 cm (2½−3 in) wide yellow flowers (capitula) have a flat receptacle. They come singly in the leaf axils, usually with several at the end of the stem. Besides a longish hypogynous ovary, the numerous disc florets have a calyx formed of many hairs, which is preserved on the fruit as a flight organ (pappus). Elecampane can be distinguished from the large yellow ox-eye (Telekia speciosa) with which it could be confused, by its smooth receptacle, which is covered with many tiny chaffy scales on the large yellow ox-eye.

Flowering time: Mid to late summer.

Habitat: Elecampane grows in damp places, especially in riverside thickets, hedges, parks and meadow ditches, as well as along forest paths and edges. It used to be cultivated particularly in rural gardens, for decorative or medicinal purposes, from which it has become established in the wild.

Distribution: This plant is probably a native of Central Asia, just gone wild from earlier cultivation throughout Europe, Asia Minor, North America and Japan.

Parts used: The rootstock and roots (Radix Helenii).

Harvesting time: Early to mid-autumn or fall.

Harvesting instructions: The rootstock of a two- or three-year-old plant is collected. It can be dried either peeled or unpeeled. Larger sections of the main root are split lengthwise. The drug should be stored in wooden boxes in a dry place; the root releases camphor of elecampane if kept in a metal container and becomes unsightly. It smells of violets, and has a bitter, spicy taste.

Ingredients: Elecampane root contains 1 to 3 per cent ethereal oil with three easily crystallising lactones, whose mixture is called Helenin or camphor of elecampane. Furthermore it contains up to 45 per cent inulin, bitter principle and pectins.

Uses: The constituents of the ethereal oil have an antibiotic effect. Helenin has antispasmodic properties and a soothing effect on dry, ticklish coughs, so the drug was used to treat respiratory diseases such as chronic bronchitis, whooping cough and tuberculosis. Because of its high inulin content it is today used in diabetic foods.

Side effects: There are no known side effects, but the root can be mistaken for deadly nightshade!

History: In antiquity elecampane was added to food as a spice, but in the Middle Ages it was often used for medicinal purposes.

Elecampane

FLAG IRIS

Iris germanica L.

Family: Iridaceae.

Description: This 30 to 100 cm (12−39 in)tall herbaceous plant survives from year to year by means of short round rootstock (rhizome). The strong stems extend beyond the leaves and are branched from about halfway up. The leaves are sword-shaped and usually curved like a sickle. Of the three to five violet to blue flowers the lower ones have long stems, the upper ones short stems. The bracteate head contains two similar components, i.e. sepals and petals are indistinguishable. The lower part of the three somewhat darker outer petals (falls) has a yellow beard on its upper side; they are white at the base and marked with dark veins. The inner ones (standards) are lighter. The tripartite fruit capsule contains many seeds.

Flowering time: Late spring to early summer.

Habitat: The flag iris is to be found on stony partly shadowed slopes, in vineyards, on walls and even on thatched roofs (in the South Tyrol up to the 1200 m (3900 ft) contour). But everywhere this is the cultivated form gone wild.

Distribution: The plant is probably a hybrid that originated in the Mediterranean area. Because of its very early cultivation it has become fully established in many places.

Parts used: Rootstock (Rhizoma Iridis).

Harvesting time: Late summer.

Harvesting instructions: The rhizomes of two- or three-year-old plants are dug up and carefully washed. After removing the root-lets the outermost corky layer is scraped off and the herb is dried in the sun. It smells of violets and tastes aromatic and irritating.

Ingredients: The herb contains 0.1 to 0.2 per cent ethereal oil, whose main constituents are myristic acid and irone, which has a smell similar to violets; also isoflavonoids, among which are iridin as well as tannin and mucilage.

Uses: Flag iris root extract serves as a coating agent for mucus membranes and to improve the taste of toothpastes and tooth powders, and as a washing powder additive. It is used in the perfumery and cosmetics industries, in the liquor industry, as a flavouring for Chianti and in the tobacco industry. Its thousand-year-old use for teething children to chew on is most unhygienic, because the moist roots form an ideal nutrient base for many disease-producing organisms which are thus introduced straight into the child's mouth.

Side effects: The fresh root is locally irritating and causes vomiting.

History: Theophrastus and Pliny mention the violet root in their writings. Charlemagne instigated the cultivation of various kinds of iris. The drug was often used in the Middle Ages.

Flag Iris

WALNUT   *Juglans regia* L.

Family: Juglandaceae.

Description: The walnut tree reaches a height of 10 to 25 m (32–85 ft) and has a smooth light grey to brown bark which later turns dark and deeply fissured and sometimes falls off. The large long-stemmed aromatic smelling leaves are odd-pinnate. The male and female flowers are separate; the green male flowers hang down loosely in thick catkins up to 10 cm (4 in) long, the females form terminal clusters with one to three blooms at the ends of the twigs. The seed-bud, formed of two carpels, develops into a single-seeded spherical stone fruit, surrounded by a fleshy outer husk, green at first, becoming brown as it ripens. The inner two-part light brown woody shell conceals a two- to four-winged kernel, rich in oil.

Flowering time: Late spring.

Habitat: Because the tree is highly regarded for its nuts and valuable wood it has been planted in gardens and occasionally in streets, from the plains up to the lower levels of secondary mountain ranges. Sometimes it has naturalised in lightly-wooded forests and on slopes.

Distribution: The walnut tree's homeland is the eastern Balkan Peninsula and Turkey. It had been introduced into Central Europe by the ninth century. Today it grows over most of Europe.

Parts used: Leaves (Folia Juglandis).

Harvesting time: Early to mid summer.

Harvesting instructions: The leaflets are stripped from their stems and dried. The herb smells slightly aromatic and tastes rough and bitter.

Ingredients: Walnut leaves contain tannin, some ethereal oil, flavonoids, vitamin C and hydrojuglone-4-glucoside, which very easily turns into juglone.

Uses: Folia juglandis is no longer used today. Because of its tannin content the herb has astringent properties. It was therefore used in the treatment of catarrh of the stomach and intestine, and externally for chilblains. Fresh walnut leaves keep insects away. Juglone, which is poisonous to seedlings and fungi, is used as a dyestuff; it dyes the hair and skin brown, and is added to skin tanning creams.

Side effects: Jugline produces blisters on the skin, and after it has turned black the epidermis peels off.

History: In antiquity it was mainly the fruit and fruit husks that were used therapeutically. Galen also used the leaves which were in general use in the early Middle Ages.

Walnut

*COMMON JUNIPER　　*Juniperus communis* L.

Family: Cupressaceae.
Description: Juniper grows into a cylindrical shrub or small tree. It is generally 100 to 150 cm (39−60 in) high, occasionally up to 5 m (16 ft). The branches of the shrubby growth usually sit on the ground. The bark later becomes flaky and partially peels off in fibres. The bluish-green leaves are arranged above each other in tripartite whorls, are sharply pointed and usually have a longitudinal groove on the keel. The blooms are dioecious, with males and females on separate plants. The very short-stemmed yellow male blooms consist of several whorls. The female carpels become fleshy and enclose three seeds in a round berry-like cone. The blackish-frosted berries ripen in their second year. There are many forms, varying in growth, needles and berry-like cones.
Flowering time: Mid to late spring.
Habitat: Juniper grows on both chalky and acid soils on dry infertile slopes, on pastures, heathland and moors and as undergrowth in light coniferous woodland from the plains to the high Alps.
Distribution: The plant is native to the whole of Europe, Northern Asia to Northern China, North America and North Africa.
Parts used: Fruits (Fructus Juniperi).
Harvesting time: Late summer to early autumn or fall.
Harvesting instructions: When gathering the ripe berries, take care not to crush them or damage the shrubs. They are dried in a heated room. The drug smells pleasantly spicy and tastes spicy and slightly sweet.
Ingredients: Juniper berries contain about 30 per cent inverted sugar, resins, tannin and flavonoidal compounds and 0.2 to 2 per cent ethereal oil, oleum juniperi, the main ingredients of which are terpineol, pinene, cadinene and camphene.
Uses: The drug was often prescribed for its diuretic effect resulting from the ethereal oil, particularly its terpineol content. It is advantageously used in combination with other diuretic drugs for chronic pyelitis and as a urine disinfectant for inflammation of the bladder. The drug can also be used externally as a skin irritant. Juniper berries are used as a spice and for producing juniper schnapps (gin).
Side effects: The drug seriously irritates the kidneys and must not be administered to kidney patients and pregnant women. External application leads to inflammation of the skin with the formation of blisters.
History: The drug was not common in medicine in antiquity, but was widely used in the Middle Ages.

Common Juniper

†SAVIN   *Juniperus sabina* (L.) GARCKE

Family: Cupressaceae.

Description: This usually 4.5 m (15 ft) high shrub has either a trunk that struggles upwards on the slant and an irregular crown, or many low-lying branches with upward-growing tips. The bark on young branches is yellowish-brown, but on older ones has a dull and flaky finish. The branches are very dense and bushy. The male and female blooms are carried at the ends of the little twigs. The fruit is a berry-like cone, the size of a pea, which becomes bluish-black the following spring. Savin is known for its dense, bushy growth, the evil smell of its crushed foliage and its fairly small drooping berry-like cones.

Flowering time: Mid to late spring.

Habitat: Savin is found scattered on warm, sunny mountainsides and cliffs or as undergrowth in Scots pine forests (up to about 2500 m (8200 ft). In West Germany it is found only in Upper Bavaria.

Distribution: This shrub is found in the mountains of Southern Europe, the Alps, the Carpathians, Turkey, the Caucasus and the southern Urals, and also sparsely on the plains of Russia and Siberia.

Parts used: Tips of branches (Summitates Sabinae).

Harvesting time: Mid to late spring.

Harvesting instructions: The youngest leafy branch tips are gathered and dried. The drug has a strong aromatic smell, like that of juniper. The taste is disagreeable, strongly aromatic and bitter.

Beware! All parts of the plant are poisonous, but especially the young shoots!

Ingredients: The savin tips contain 3 to 5 per cent ethereal oil, the main ingredients being sabinol and sabinol acetate and also sabinene, cadinene and pinene. Furthermore, the drug contains tannin, resin and the bitter glycoside pinipicrin.

Uses: The drug is no longer used internally because of its toxicity. In the past it was used as an emmenagogue and incorrectly as an abortive.

Toxic effect: The savin's ethereal oil is significantly more poisonous than that of the juniper. External application leads to severe skin damage and destroys the deeper layers of the skin. From internal use or absorption of the toxic substances, the kidneys and the urinary tracts leading from them are severely damaged, causing bleeding. In 50 per cent of poisoning cases death occurs usually after several days while the patient is deeply unconscious.

History: The effects of savin were known to Dioscorides, Pliny and Galen. Charlemagne recorded it in his "Capitulare" and Hildegard of Bingen also mentioned it.

Savin

WHITE DEAD-NETTLE　　　*Lamium album* L.

Family: Labiatae.

Description: This plant's underground rootstock survives the winter then in spring produces many flowering shoots as well as new underground runners that root as they go. The lower part of the square, loosely pilose stem, about 20 to 40 cm (8–15 in) high is often suffused reddish-violet. The opposite leaves are pilose on both sides. The inflorescences consist of three to six verticillasters, bearing 6 to 16 flowers each. The dirty white corona, as in all labiates is formed of five petals. The four dark-brown, downy white anthers lie close together under the upper lip. The long style has a bifid stigma.

Flowering time: Mid-spring to mid-autumn or fall.

Habitat: The white dead-nettle grows on rubbish tips and is also found beside paths, fences and hedgerows. It is often found in company with stinging nettles on dung-heaps and in pastures.

Distribution: The plant is widespread over most of temperate Europe and Asia, from France to Japan, and as at home in the Himalayas as in the Alps. It was introduced into North America.

Parts used: Flowers (Flores Lamii albi).

Harvesting time: Late spring to mid-summer.

Harvesting instructions: In dry weather the white blooms are carefully removed from the calyx and dried as quickly as possible in thin layers to stop them turning brown. The yellowish-white flowers have a light honey-like odour and a sweet, slimy taste.

Ingredients: The drug contains biogene amines, including choline, histamine, tyramine and methylamine; also the flavonoids querci-meritrine, camphor-3-diglucoside, lamioside and rutine. In addition tannin and mucilage.

Uses: Dead-nettle blossoms are prescribed for indigestion because they contain mucus and also for stomach and intestinal catarrh due to their astringent properties. The drug is also used for menstrual troubles.

Side effects: There are no known side effects.

History: Nothing is known about the use of dead-nettle blooms in antiquity. In the Middle Ages the drug was frequently used and mentioned in all the herbals. At that time it was employed almost exclusively for urinary retention though also for dyeing the hair yellow.

White Dead-nettle

LAVENDER   *Lavandula angustifolia* MILL.

Family: Labiatae.

Description: This small sub-shrub, about 15 to 60 cm (6—24 in) high, is upright or ascending with dense branches from which stiff upright shoots emerge, some with small young growths. In May the top of the branches bring forth new upright young shoots with opposite leaves, 2 to 5 cm (½—2 in) long. The flowering shoots grow about 60 cm (24 in) high, with leaves only on the lower part. The inflorescence usually consists of four or five verticillasters each with six to ten flowers. The violet corona grows about 1 cm long with downy glands inside and is white-felted outside. The whole plant has a pleasant scent.

Flowering time: Mid to late summer.

Habitat: In Europe lavender is mainly found in gardens.

Distribution: The lavender's home is the Western Mediterranean area, where it is widespread on dry warm slopes as far east as Dalmatia and Greece. It is also found sporadically up to the tree limit (up to 1700 m (5600 ft) in the Maritime Alps). This sub-shrub has become completely naturalised on the "Lavender Mountain" between Bingen and Kreuznach, and further afield near Jena, Rudolstadt and Bad Blankenburg. It is also known to have been growing a long time in other places.

Parts used: Flowers (Flores Lavandulae).

Harvesting time: Mid to late summer.

Harvesting instructions: The flowers and calyces are gathered without leaves and stems before they are fully open and dried in loose layers. They have a pleasant aromatic scent and a bitter taste.

Ingredients: The dried lavender flowers contain approximately 12 per cent tannin as well as up to 3 per cent ethereal oils (oleum lavandulae). Main constituents of the ethereal oils are linalylacetate and linalool. They also contain cumarin. They have a characteristic smell and a very spicy, slightly bitter taste. Real lavender oil contains no camphor in comparison to spike oil.

Uses: The flowers are used to calm nervous heart complaints and troubled sleep, and also as a cholagogue, a diuretic and a carminative. Externally the flowers, and particularly their ethereal oils, are used mainly as a skin stimulant, either as a liniment or bath additive, and also frequently as an air freshener.

Side effects: In exceptional cases it can cause headaches due to its cumarine content.

History: In antiquity the flowers of *Lavandula stoechas* were put into baths. Real lavender was first used in the Middle Ages for treating eyes and to ward off moths. Earlier, all kinds of lavender were used for an extract called spike oil. Oleum lavandulae was first distilled in the sixteenth century, and included in the 'Frankfurt Drug List' of 1582.

Lavender

MOTHERWORT

Leonurus cardiaca L.

Family: Labiate.
Description: The strong branched perennial rootstock produces a number of upright, square, metre-high often reddish violet stems. The slightly drooping leaves which are usually covered on both sides in soft hair are 7 to 14 cm (3−5½ in) long, with three lobes or three leaflets. The many-flowered verticillasters appear in tens to twenties a little way apart one above the other on the main stem to form a 15 to 30 cm (6−12 in) long dense-leaved spike. Its corlla is flesh-pink, tufted with hair and slightly longer than the calyx. The upper lip is densely covered in white hairs outside, the lower lip is shorter and consists of three brownish lobes.
Flowering time: Early summer to early autumn or fall.
Habitat: Motherwort was formerly cultivated as a healing plant in farmworkers' gardens. It can now be found scattered on rubbish tips, village greens, fences, hedges and on dry pastures.
Distribution: The plant is distributed throughout temperate Asia up to the Himalayas and to eastern Siberia. It probably became naturalised in Europe and can be found up to Central Scandinavia and in the south to the Mediterranean. It is rare south of the Alps. It was introduced into North America.
Parts used: Herbage (Herba Leonuri cardiacae).
Harvesting time: Mid summer to early autumn or fall.
Harvesting instructions: Motherwort herbage was cut off while in flower near or far from the ground according to its size and dried carefully. The drug is odourless and tastes sharp, bitter and astringent.
Ingredients: The drug contains bitter constituents, leonurin, tannin, resin, organic acids and a little ethereal oil, alkaloids (stachydrin, betonicin and leonurin) as well as flavonoids.
Uses: The drug is said to be a cardiotonic. In folk medicine it was used as a sedative for nervous and functional heart complaints as well as an emmenagogue.
Side effects: There are no known side effects.
History: Motherwort was mentioned by Theophrastus and Dioscorides. The medicinal values of the plant were also known during the Middle Ages and it appeared in the herbals.

Motherwort

LOVAGE   *Levisticum officinale* KOCH

Family: Umbelliferae.

Description: Lovage is a perennial herb with a thick, branched rootstock marked with rings. From the basal leaf rosette, the first part to appear in spring, develops the 1–2 m (3–6½ ft) high stem up to 4 cm (1½ in) thick at ground level. It is tubular, the upper part grooved with upright projecting branches. The lower leaves carried on narrow-tubed stems are bi- or tripartite and can grow up to 70 cm (28 in) long and 65 cm (25½ in) wide. The flowers are borne in umbels each of 10 to 20 rays at the ends of the branches. The smallish yellow-green hermaphrodite flowers lack calyces. The whole plant has a strong smell of celery.

Flowering time: Mid to late summer.

Habitat: Lovage is particularly popular as a culinary herb in gardens from which it has now gone wild.

Distribution: The plant is cultivated in large parts of Europe and North America where it also has gone wild. But it is not known as a truly wild plant anywhere. The mountain ranges of Iran seem to be the original homeland of lovage.

Parts used: Root (Radix Levistici).

Harvesting time: Mid-autumn or fall.

Harvesting instructions: Two- to three-year-old roots are harvested, cleaned and if necessary split longitudinally, then dried at temperatures up to 40°C. The drug must be stored in airtight containers. It has a penetrating spicy smell and tastes first sweet, later spicy and finally bitter.

Ingredients: The lovage root contains 0.6–1 per cent ethereal oil, which consists of up to 70 per cent phthaliden, terpineol and also resin, gum, angelica acid, benzoic acid, malic acid, cumarin, starch and sugar.

Uses: The drug has a pharmacologically proven strong diuretic effect and is listed in medicinal books as an ingredient of tea mixtures for washing out the patient. In folk medicine lovage was also used as a stomachic. In addition it is used as a spice and in the liquor industry.

Side effects: Using the drug can cause kidney irritation and should therefore not be used by those suffering from kidney complaints.

History: Dioscorides mentions the effects of this drug, which was also praised in Charlemagne's 'Capitulare'. The plant has maintained its position in medical science from the Middle Ages to the present day.

Lovage

TOADFLAX   *Linaria vulgaris* MILL.

Family: Scrophulariaceae.

Description: The common toadflax is a perennial herbaceous plant that overwinters by means of its creeping cylindrical rootstock. Early in the year this produces an upright stem clothed with alternate leaves that occasionally branch from the base and grow up to 60 cm (2 ft) high. The blossoms are crowded together in clustered inflorescences at the ends of the stems. Each flower arises from the axil of a bract. The light yellow corolla has an orange-coloured palate, a cleft upper lip and a three-lobed underlip. One of the petals forms a spur containing nectar. Bumble bees are the main pollinators.

Flowering time: Early summer to early autumn or fall.

Habitat: Because of its vigorous propagating potential — one plant can have over 30,000 seeds — toadflax can be a troublesome weed. It colonises railway embankments, roadside verges, rubbish tips, arable and fallow land, sand and river-gravel from the lowlands to highlands 1600 m (4800 ft) above sea level.

Distribution: This plant can be found throughout Europe (with the exception of the far north) and eastwards as far as Western Asia.

Parts used: Herbage (Herba Linariae).

Harvesting time: Summer.

Harvesting instructions: The herbage minus the lower part of the stem is picked while in bloom and carefully dried. The taste is bitter at first, then pungent.

Ingredients: Common toad flax contains biologically active substances, flavonoids, and amongst others, linarin, pectolinarin and neolinarin. It contains other substances called amygdalin, gum and pectin.

Uses: This drug is no longer in use today. In the past it was used as a diuretic and in the form of a cream for the relief of painful haemorrhoids.

Side effects: Even tiny doses of tincture of toadflax cause watery diarrhoea.

History: Toadflax is an ancient healing plant that was once in frequent use.

Toadflax

FLAX

Linum usitatissimum L.

Family: Linaceae.

Description: This annual or biennial plant, 20−100 cm (8−39 in) high, has a thin spindly root. From this emerge single or sometimes several densely leaved stems, some of them branched towards the top. The flowers are borne at the ends of the shoots on long upright stems. They flower for only one day and when in full flower lift their heads from their nodding position. The underside of the sky-blue darker-veined petals is yellowish, white, light-blue, pink or lilac. The seedpod usually contains 10 shiny oval seeds.

Flowering time: Early to mid-summer.

Habitat: Flax is less frequently cultivated in fields today than it once was. It flourishes from the plains to the Alps up to 1800m and also grows on wasteland, in cereal-fields and field boundaries. Yet it is extremely variable and has not become naturalised anywhere.

Distribution: The cultivated plant stems from the wild flax, which grows in the Mediterranean area.

Parts used: Seeds (Semen Lini).

Harvesting time: Late summer to early autumn or fall.

Harvesting instructions: The seedpods are harvested when they turn brown and the seeds are removed by machine-threshing. The drug is odourless and has a mild, slimy, oily taste.

Ingredients: The flax seeds contain approximately 35 per cent fatty oil and about 0.3 per cent of the cyanogen glycoside, linamarin and lotaustralin as well as the enzyme linamarase and, in the epidermis of the seed shell, about 5 per cent mucilage. The oil from the pressed seeds contains glyceride of the linoleic acids, linoleic acid and oil acid as well as palmitic and stearic acid.

Uses: The whole or crushed seeds are prescribed as a mild and harmless laxative. The swelling of the mucilage increases the volume and stimulates the contractions of the bowel. The oil from the crushed seeds aids evacuation. The hydrocyanic acid released in small quantities by the cyanogen glycosides has a local analgesic effect, is anti-inflammatory and checks the spread of sepsis. Flax seed powder, the residue from the extraction method and particularly the oil, were used externally. The former was used for poultices and the oil for skin diseases such as eczema and burns.

Side effects: Poisoning with whole seeds is not possible, but ingesting 200g or more of powdered seeds can be fatal.

History: Flax has been cultivated for 5,000 years.

Flax

*COMMON CLUB MOSS *Lycopodium clavatum* L.

Family: Lycopodiaceae.

Description: The stems of common club moss spread for more than 1 m (3 ft) like stolons. They have bifurcated roots on the Like all club mosses the evergreen growth divides into climbing branches and is closely covered with spirally arranged incurving leaflets. These are drawn out into fine, colourless hairlike ties which clearly distinguish it from other species. The 2 to 4 cm (½– 1½ in) long cone-shaped upright sporophyll stems generally come in pairs at the ends of the shoots. The sporangia within them release myriads of spores which take six or seven years to germinate and form an embryo (seedling).

Spores Mature: Mid to late summer.

Habitat: Common club moss is found on heaths, in old quarries, on hillsides, in dry coniferous woodland, always in mainly sandy soil deficient in lime from the plains to the Alpine regions (up to about 2300 m (7550 ft).

Distribution: Apart from the steppes and the evergreen vegetation of the Mediterranean, common club moss is found all over Europe.

Parts used: Spores (Lycopodium).

Harvesting time: Late summer to early autumn or fall.

Harvesting instructions: To harvest the spores the fertile spikes are picked and dried in the sun, then threshed on a sheet so the spores drop out. They are then sieved to clean them of any impurities. The drug is odourless and tasteless.

Ingredients: Club moss spores, which form a very fine loose powder, contain up to 50 per cent fatty oil, 20 per cent sporonin, acids, resin, gum and traces of alkaloids.

Uses: In former times the drug was used internally as a diuretic. Later it was long used exclusively as a pharmacologically ineffective material as a dusting powder for pills. Lycopodium spores were used in technology to test grinding machines and as flash powder in the theatre.

Side effects: The club moss plant's herbage contains more than 3 per cent toxic alkaloids.

History: In Bock's herbal (1546) this plant was referred to as "*Beerlap*". The first medical use was reported in the sixteenth century and wounds were dusted with it. Since that time pills have also been dusted with lycopodium spores.

Common Club Moss

SWEET MARJORAM   *Origanum marjorana* L.

Family: Labiatae.

Description: This 15 to 40 cm (2—15 in) tall sub-shrub is generally grown as an annual in Central Europe. The many-branched stems are relatively slender but tough. All the green parts of the plant have a downy to tomentose covering, so the herbage appears grey-green to white. The stems are often suffused a reddish colour. The verticillasters of the clustered inflorescences are mostly covered with circular involucral leaves beyond which the flowers hardly project at all. The corollas of the flowers are white to pale lilac or pink. The seeds are up to 1 mm long, like small light brown nuts. In Central Europe the seeds ripen only in the warmest places. There are various types of marjoram, distinguished as annual and perennial, for their early or late maturity, and the strength of their aroma.

Flowering time: Mid-summer to early autumn or fall.

Habitat: This frost-sensitive plant likes light soils and is grown mainly in herb gardens and cultivated agriculturally.

Distribution: Marjoram is found from Western India via Arabia and Egypt to Tripoli and is partially naturalised in the Mediterranean region. It is also cultivated in Europe and America.

Parts used: Flowering herbage (Herba Majoranae).

Harvesting time: Mid-summer to early autumn or fall.

Harvesting instructions: The plant is cut off about 20 cm (8 in) above the soil and dried in a thin layer. The drug smells pleasantly spicy like camphor and tastes bitter and aromatic.

Ingredients: Marjoram contains about 0.7 per cent ethereal oil with thymol, carvacrol and other substances including tannin and bitter constituents.

Uses: The drug was once used as a stomachic, antispadmodic and diuretic. It was occasionally used externally as an additive to linament for gout and rheumatism, but especially as 'marjoram butter' to treat babies' colds. Marjoram was used far more often as a spice, particularly in the manufacture of sausages.

Side effects: The fresh herbage can cause skin and eye inflammation.

History: Marjoram is an old medicinal herb. It is assumed that it was cultivated and used in Arabia and Egypt. It has been used in Europe since the sixteenth century.

Sweet Marjoram

DWARF MALLOW   *Malva neglecta* WALLR.

Family: Malvaceae.

Description: The dwarf mallow is an annual or perennial herbaceous plant about 10—45 cm (4—18 in) long with a thin taproot. Its branched stems are mostly prostrate or ascending. The round to kidney-shaped leaf blade, divided into five to seven indistinct lobes, is attached by its cordate base to the petiole up to 27 cm (10½ in) long. The flowers are borne singly or several together in the axils of the leaves on pedicels up to 4 cm (2 in) long. The light pink to nearly white corolla is twice the depth of the calyx. When ripe the ovary disintegrates into single-seeded partial fruits.

Flowering time: Early summer to mid-autumn or fall.

Habitat: This plant's occurrence on walls, rubbish tips and pathways is closely linked with human influence. It grows from the plains to the mountains.

Distribution: In Europe the dwarf mallow can be found as far north as Central Scandinavia, Southern Finland and Southern Karelia, and further east from Western Asia to Lake Baikal and Tibet to Western India. In the south the plant can be found as far as North Africa. It was introduced into Australia, South America and North America by the colonists.

Parts used: Leaves (Folia Malvae).

Harvesting time: Early summer.

Harvesting instructions: The leaves are collected and dried in a thin layer in a well ventilated room. The drug dries quickly and easily. It is odourless and has a herby slimy taste. Dwarf mallow leaves, together with those of the common mallow (Malva sylvestris L.), form the official drug.

Ingredients: The leaves of the dwarf mallow contain mucilage and tannin.

Uses: Because of its mucilage and tannin content the drug was used for catarrh, angina and stomach and intestine inflammations.

Side effects: There are no known side effects.

History: The mallow leaves' high mucilage content drew the doctors' attention in antiquity to this drug, which is used internally and externally as an enveloping agent. It was also recommended for insect bites. Pliny reported that the leaves of the dwarf mallow were used as a vegetable. Mallow species were highly respected as a medicine during the Middle Ages and were frequently prescribed.

Dwarf Mallow

COMMON MALLOW   *Malva sylvestris* L.

Family: Malvaceae.

Description: Common mallow grows to a height of 150 cm (5 ft) but the stem often lies on the ground and bends upwards at the end. The plant may be biennial or perennial. The stems are covered in numerous tufts of hair and filled with loose pith. The outside of the lower part of the plant becomes woody. The grass-green leaves have three to seven lobes. The flowers form groups of two to six in the leaf axils. Each of the five pinkish violet petals grow together as a tube from which the style protrudes. The disc-shaped fruit disintegrates when ripe into 9 to 11 partial fruits. This species differs from the similar dwarf mallow by the different length of the petals which, in the common mallow are three to five times the length of the calyx.

Flowering time: Early summer to mid-autumn or fall.

Habitat: In Central Europe the distribution of common mallow is closely linked with human habitations. It grows on rubbish tips, waste ground, on walls, by footpaths and fences and so on.

Distribution: The common mallow probably originated in Southern Europe and Central Asia. It is cultivated in India, and was introduced by settlers into America, Australia and South Africa.

Parts used: Flowers (Flores Malvae), leaves (Folia Malvae).

Harvesting time: Flowers, July to September, leaves, June to September.

Harvesting instructions: The flowers are gathered without their stems.They become a dark blue while drying. The leaves are often covered in brownish spots caused by a parasitic fungus. The drug is odourless and has a slimy taste.

Ingredients: The flowers of the common mallow contain mucilage, tannin and anthocyan colouring such as malvine. The content of the leaves is mucilage and tannin.

Uses: Due to its mucilage content the drug is a good medicine for respiratory complaints and is also prescribed in paediatrics. Its tannin also makes it effective for inflammations of the gastro-intestinal tract. The blue flowers, like those of the rose mallow, are used as dyes in the food industry.

Side effects: No side effects are known.

History: The plant was mentioned by Hesiod in 700 BC. Dioscorides recommended it for burns. Charlemagne promoted the cultivation of common mallow, which was often used as a medicine during the Middle Ages.

Common Mallow

GERMAN CHAMOMILE
Matricaria chamomilla L.

Family: Compositae.
Description: This annual plant grows up to 55 cm (21½ in) high with an erect, usually branching stem, with the flowers at the ends. On its initially flat and later conically elongated, hollow receptacle are arranged the golden-yellow quinate disc florets, each surrounded by a circle of white ray florets. These soon fold back as the receptacle enlarges during flowering.
Flowering time: Late spring to early autumn or fall.
Habitat: The plant flourishes particularly in places influenced by human activity such as meadows, fields, waste ground and paths, from the plains to the alpine valleys. It was also cultivated on agricultural land and in herb gardens.
Distribution: German chamomile grows in most parts of Europe to about latitude 60° north. Across Turkey, Iran and India it can be followed all the way to China. It was introduced into North America and Australia.
Parts used: Flowerheads (Flores Chamomillae).
Harvesting time: Late spring to late summer.
Harvesting instructions: The flowerheads were collected while in full bloom on a sunny day during the middle of the day and dried in a well ventilated room or at temperatures of up to 40°C. They should not be turned. The drug has a characteristic aromatic scent and tastes aromatic and slightly bitter.
Ingredients: Steam distillation of the chamomile flowers provides 0.5 to 1.5 per cent of an ethereal oil coloured blue by chamazulen. Chamazulen is produced out of proazulen matricin via the intermediate stage of chamazulen carbolic acid. Other important substances of the oil are bisabolol, the Bisabololoxides and farnesen. The drug also contains flavonglycosides, for example apigenin- and Luteolin-7-glucoside; derivates of cumarin such as umbelliferon and herniarin, choline, polyins and mucins.
Uses: Chamomile is one of the best known household remedies listed in virtually every pharmacopoeia and has a wide application. In the first place its effect is anti-inflammatory due to the bisabolol and bisabololoxide, chamazulen and farnesen it contains. Its antispasmodic effects depend on the flavon glycosides and cumarin derivatives. The chamomile flowers or their ethereal oil (Oleum Chamomillae) are prescribed externally for inflammations, burns, wounds, boils and as a mouthwash. Infusions or extracts are also used for inhalations, and are used internally for their antispasmodic and carminative effects in the cases of gastritis and gastric ulcers.
Side effects: No side effects are known.
History: Chamomile flowers have often been used since antiquity. Chamomile oil was mentioned for the first time in 1588.

German Chamomile

YELLOW MELILOT *Melilotus altissima* THUILL.

Family: Papilionaceae.

Description: Yellow melilot is a biennial with a vigorous taproot, which usually produces a single erect branched stem up to 150 cm (5 ft) high. The upper part of the plant carries a many-flowered clustered inflorescence in every axil of its trifoliate leaves. In the brilliant yellow corolla one can clearly distinguish an upper petal called the standard, two lateral ones referred to as wings and a so-called keel. In M. officinalis (L. PALLAS), also used medicinally, the wings are shorter than the keel and the ovary is smooth (hairy in M. altissima). M. dentata, which has toothed stipulate leaves, is similar to these two species and is found on saline soils.

Flowering time: Melilotus altissima, mid-summer to early autumn or fall; M. officinalis, late spring to early autumn or fall.

Habitat: Melilots are found beside paths and fields, on walls, in vineyards, on rubbish dumps and in slightly saline soils. M. altissima prefers moist places and is less common than M. officinalis.

Distribution: M. altissima seems to be the only species native to most of Europe, and is found from Spain to France to Eastern Europe, in the north to Scandinavia and the Gulf of Finland, and across the Urals and Siberia to Japan.

Parts used: Herbage (Herba Meliloti).

Harvesting time: Early summer to early autumn or fall.

Harvesting instructions: The flowering shoots are cut off about 20 cm (8 in) long then bundled and dried. They should not change colour during this process. The drug Herba Meliloti consists of the herbage of M. altissima and M. officinalis. It smells like woodruff and has an aromatic bitter salty taste.

Ingredients: The main constituent of the drug is cumarin which is also present in the woodruff exuding its peculiar odour. The fresh plant contains melilotosid which is odourless and produces cumarin enzymatically during the drying process. In addition the herbage contains mucilage, resin and tannin and the flowers some 0.01 per cent ethereal oil.

Uses: The drug was formerly used as an antispasmodic and an anti-inflammatory agent. It was prescribed for external treatment of swollen joints and glands, rheumatism and ulcers. Cumarin is nowadays produced synthetically as a deodorant.

Side effects: There is no danger of poisonings from plants containing cumarin although headaches and giddiness can occur.

History: The drug was frequently prescribed in antiquity, particularly for external use. Other species of melilot were also used.

Yellow Melilot

LEMON BALM   *Melissa officinalis* L.

Family: Labiatae.

Description: This herbaceous plant up to 80 cm (32 in) high, grows from a many-branched perennial rootstock, with numerous upright, many-branched stems bearing widely spaced leaves. The projecting or slightly nodding flowers are bluish to yellowish-white and appear in the leaf axils as compressed verticillasters. The plant has a lemony smell.

Flowering time: Summer.

Habitat: Lemon balm is often cultivated in herb gardens and on a field scale. It also grows round the outskirts of woods, in hedges, by fences, on walls, in vineyards and on rubbish tips. In mountain regions it is often found fully naturalised.

Distribution: This plant, known since olden times as food for bees, as a herb and medicinal plant, came from the East. It was probably originally distributed from the Eastern Mediterranean area via the Caucasus and Iran to South-West Siberia. It has established itself in the alpine countries. Besides Europe and temperate Asia, it is nowadays often cultivated in North America.

Parts used: Leaves (Folia Melissae).

Harvesting time: Summer.

Harvesting instructions: The shoots are cut off before flowering about 10 cm (4 in) above the ground and the leaves stripped. They should be dried in warm air at up to 40°C and turned several times. Leaves of flowering plants should not be collected since the plant's effective ingredients alter during flowering. The drug has a lemony smell and a weak lemony, slightly spicy taste. The plant gives off an unpleasant smell while in flower.

Ingredients: The melilot leaves contain 0.01 to 0.3 per cent ethereal oil, the citronellal, citral, geraniol and linalool. Other ingredients are bitter constituents, tannin and mucilage.

Uses: The drug is a sedative, anti-convulsive and carminative.The main areas of application are nervous disorders of the stomach, intestines and heart. The drug is often a constituent of sedative decoctions. Externally it is used for wounds, neuralgia and rheumatism. Lemon balm is also used as a culinary herb.

Side effects: Lemon balm leaves have a mild effect and were used in paediatrics.

History: Lemon balm was known to medicine at the time of the Greeks and Romans, though under a different name. Disocorides describes its healing effects. It was introduced into Spain by the Arabs during the tenth century and soon afterwards arrived in Central Europe. At the beginning of the sixteenth century the herbage and lemon balm water were already used medicinally. Lemon balm oil appears in the official list of Frankfurt dated 1582.

Lemon Balm

PEPPERMINT   *Mentha piperita* L.

Family: Labiatae.

Description: The square stem grows upright, up to 80 cm (32 in) high, and has a thickened woody rootstock at the base. The shoots often suffused a reddish colour, the leaves have distinct stems and sharply serrated margins. The lilac flowers usually appear in rather loose cymose spikes. Since the plant is ia hybrid it can only be propagated from its creeping stolons. It has a spicy smell.

Flowering time: Early to mid-summer.

Habitat: Peppermint has become naturalised in some damp meadows and near water but nowhere is it a native plant.

Distribution: Peppermint is cultivated in most of Europe (northwards as far as Southern Sweden) as well as in North and South American.

Parts used: Leaves (Folia Menthae piperitae).

Harvesting time: Early to mid-summer.

Harvesting instructions: Before flowering begins the entire shoots are cut off about 20 cm (8 in) above ground level. The leaves are then stripped off and spread out with the shoot tips in a thin layer to dry. Any pieces of stem should be cut off. Warm air up to 40°C is suitable for this purpose. Any leaves with spores of the rust fungus on the underside must be discarded. The drug has a penetrating, pleasant aromatic smell and a spicy burning taste with a cooling after-taste.

Ingredients: Peppermint leaves contain 1 to 3 per cent ethereal oil, tannin, bitter constituents and flavonoids. The ethereal oil (Oleum Menthae piperitae) consists of 50 per cent menthol. The smell and taste of the oil are due to the menthylester. Other ingredients of the oil are cineol and menthon. The extracts of drugs which are collected during flowering have a sharp and unpleasant smelling oil which contains menthofuran.

Uses: Peppermint leaves are among the most commonly used drugs. The effect is based on the anti-convulsive, carminative and choleretic as well as disinfecting characteristics of the ethereal oil. The choloretic effect is due to the flavonoid content, while the tannin in the leaves is effective against diarrhoea. The drug is prescribed for loss of appetite, to stimulate the digestion, for gallstones, gastritis, flatulence and colic. It is an ingredient of various tea mixtures, particularly for stomach, liver and gall-bladder decoctions. Pure menthol has a cooling, analgesic and astringent effect on the mucus membranes and the skin.

Side effects: Larger doses of menthol cause inflammations of the gastro-intestinal tract. Peppermint leaves have no side effects.

History: Peppermint was bred from other species of mint in 1696. The mints are very old healing plants.

Peppermint

CURLED WATERMINT
Mentha spicata var. *crispata* (SCHRAD.) BECK

Family: Labiatae.

Description: When in flower curled watermint stands 30−60 cm (1-2 ft) high. It survives from year to year by means of its stolons. The square stem is ascending or upright and partially branched, usually shortly before the flowers are formed. The opposite leaves are arranged in a cruciform pattern and their margins fringed with teeth. The spike-shaped inflorescences are arranged in verticillasters borne in the axils of the bracts. The five pointed bright-lilac corolla is nearly twice as tall as the five-toothed coarsely hairy calyx. The whole plant has a strong aromatic smell.

Flowering time: Late summer to early autumn or fall.

Habitat: Curled watermint is frequently found in gardens and is also cultivated on a larger scale.

Distribution: This plant has become naturalised in many areas, such as Alsace, the Rhineland, in the Harz mountains, (Rubeland, Blankenburg and Ballenstedt) and especially in Thuringia.

Parts used: Leaves (Folia Menthae crispae).

Harvesting time: Early summer to early autumn or fall.

Harvesting instructions: Besides the leaves of curled watermint, those of other curled-leaf mints, generally cultivated, are collected. The drug must be dried quickly in a well ventilated, shady place. It has a slight aromatic smell and a spicy burning taste, but without the cooling aftertaste of peppermint.

Ingredients: The leaves of the crisp/curled watermint contain disomin, apigenin, luteolin, hesperidin, tannin and bitter constituents and produce, during water distillation, 1−2.5 per cent ethereal oil (Oleum menthae crispae). The main constituent of the ethereal oil is carvon, other constituents are cineol, limonen and phellandres. Its pleasant aromatic smell is attributed to the ingredient dihydrocuminylacetate and dihydrocarveolacetate. Since it does not contain menthol, the cooling aftertaste of the peppermint is missing.

Uses: Curled watermint is used, like peppermint, for complaints in the gastro-intestinal tract, such as colic and flatulence, though not so frequently. The drug promotes secretions and encourages the appetite. The ethereal oil of the curled watermint has the same effect as the leaves and is added to chewing gum, toothpaste, mouth washes and confectionery.

Side effects: No side effects are known.

History: The various types of mint were popular healing plants in antiquity because of their strong aroma. They also played a role in those peoples' worship.

Curled Watermint

BOGBEAN   *Menyanthes trifoliata* L.

Family: Gentianaceae.
Description: The bogbean survives for many years by means of its segmented rootstock, which is branched and covered in scaly bracts. In spring a short leafy shoot emerges. The few leaves are long petiolated. The ray-like hermaphrodite flowers are grouped in an inflorescence on a long stem up to 30 cm (1 ft) in length. The tender, slightly fleshy, short funnel-shaped corolla is pink tinted and split into five lobes to the centre. It has rolled back tips and many succulent hairs on the inside. Five stamens with dark violet, arrow-shaped, split anthers are inserted in the corolla tube.
Flowering time: Late spring to early summer up to late summer in the Alps.
Habitat: The bogbean is mainly found on flat bogland, in wet meadows and by the water's edge on river banks. It grows in the lowlands and up into the alpine foothills (in Bavaria up to 1800 m (5900 ft)) but is rarely found on chalky soil.
Distribution: This plant grows all over Europe and temperate Asia, eastwards to Japan and to northern North America.
Parts used: Leaves (Folia trifolii fibrini).
Harvesting time: Late spring to mid-summer.
Harvesting instructions: The bogbean leaves are cut off while it is in flower with a short length of the petiole and spread out to dry in a thin layer in a well ventilated room. Any discoloured pieces are discarded. The drug is nearly odourless and has a strong and lasting bitter taste.
Ingredients: The leaves of the drug contain, as effective ingredients, the bitter constituent glycosides like menyanthin. Other ingredients are tannin, pectin, saponin, some ethereal oil, alkaloids such as gentianin and vitamin C. The bitter value of the drug is between 1500 and 10,000.
Uses: The drug is, like Gentiana lutea, prescribed exclusively as a bitter agent. Taken half an hour before mealtimes it stimulates the appetite and helps the digestion. As a sedative bogbean is sometimes included with peppermint and valerian in nerve decoctions. The drug is no longer a significant antipyretic.
Side effects: Poisoning from this plant is unheard of, but in exceptional cases it could cause stomach upsets.
History: The plant was illustrated and described for the first time in the sixteenth century, though under different names, such as Trifolium fibrinum. Though already popular, it was not used medicinally before the end of the seventeenth century.

Bogbean

WATERCRESS   *Nasturtium officinale* R. BR.

Family: Cruciferae.

Description: Watercress is a 30–90 cm (12–35 in) water plant that can grow even longer. Its roots disappear early and are replaced by horizontal creeping, many rooted stolons. From these emerge rising, square stems bearing pinnate, grass-green leaves. The foliage shoots terminate in clustered inflorescences. Each of the four white petals narrows down into a long narrow stem (claw). They are longer than the sepals. The small seeds, up to 1 mm across, are often distributed by water birds. The leaves have a sharp radish-like taste.

Flowering time: Late spring to late summer and sporadically in mid-autumn or fall.

Habitat: Watercress grows in water-rich areas or where there are springs. It prefers to colonise brooks fed by springs, and rivers and ditches filled with clean water, seldom stagnant waters. It is cultivated on a large scale.

Distribution: Watercress is cosmopolitan, being at home all over the world. In Europe it is found as far north as the Island of Gotland and Denmark and eastwards to Western Poland and the Carpathian Mountains.

Parts used: Herbage (Herba Nasturtii).

Harvesting time: Early spring to early autumn or fall.

Harvesting instructions: The herbage is collected without its flowers at flowering time. The older leaves are discarded as they become discoloured when dried. The fresh drug has a sharp spicy smell and a sharp spicy radish-like taste. It loses both taste and smell when dried.

Ingredients: The fresh herbage contains the mustard oil glycoside glyconasturtiin and during decomposition develops phenylethyli-sothiocyanate (mustard oil) which is the main constituent of the ethereal oil. It also contains the locally strong irritant raphanol, tannin and vitamins such as vitamin C.

Uses: Watercress herbage is a diuretic, is sometimes used as a "blood cleanser" and is a source of vitamins. Because of the mustard oil's anti-biotic and digestant characteristics the fresh herbage is a valuable spice.

Side effects: Raphanol can cause a burning sensation in the urinary canals. When this occurs the so-called "spring treatment" should be discontinued.

History: The medicinal effects of watercress as a healing and spice plant were known to medicine in antiquity. In Paracelsus' time it was also used as a vermifuge, for scurvy, tuberculosis, bleeding, kidney troubles, colds, asthma and other complaints.

Watercress

LOVE-IN-A-MIST

Nigella damascena L.

Family: Ranunculaceae.

Description: This roughly 30 cm (1 ft) high plant has a vertical root and a sparsely branched stem clothed with alternate, multi-pinnatifid leaves and bearing flowers at the top. These have five light blue to white, greenish tipped sepals surrounded by a crown of protruding pinnatifid bracts with subulate sections. They enclose many yellow stamens and an ovary with almost horizontal spreading styles which unite with the five carpels. In contrast to love-in-a-mist, common love-in-a-mist (*Nigella sativa* L.), also used medicinally, has bracts enveloping its milk-white petals, which are greenish or bluish at the tips. The love-in-a-mist fruit is a many-seeded blister-like follicle. The dark triangular seeds have a spicy smell.

Flowering time: Summer.

Habitat: Love-in-a-mist is a highly popular decorative plant. The common love-in-a-mist, rare nowadays, used to be cultivated in farm gardens and also in the fields.

Distribution: These various species, native to the Mediterranean area, are either cultivated or have become naturalised in Central Europe.

Parts used: Seeds (Semen Nigellae sativae; Semen Nigellae damascenae).

Harvesting time: Early autumn or fall.

Harvesting instructions: The seeds of both species of love-in-a-mist are collected and dried. Seeds of the field love-in-a-mist (*Nigella arvensis* L.) must not be mixed with the harvested material as they are useless. The seeds of the common love-in-a-mist have a camphor-like small reminiscent of nutmeg when ground down. Those of the love-in-a-mist have a pleasant strawberry-like fragrance. The drug has a bitter taste at first, but becomes sharp and spicy.

Ingredients: The common love-in-mist contains 0.5 to 1.5 per cent ethereal oil with thymochinon, the bitter constituent nigellin, saponins and tannin. The love-in-mist contains 0.4–0.5 per cent ethereal oil with approximately 9 per cent of the alkaloid damascenin.

Uses: Love-in-a-mist was once used as a diuretic and a carminative but nowadays the seeds are employed mainly as a spice.

Side effects: Due to their low content of effective ingredients the seeds have no side effects. Damascenin stimulates the secretion of saliva and has a central narcotic effect.

History: The Arabs, Greeks and Romans used love-in-a-mist, which was also used in the Middle Ages.

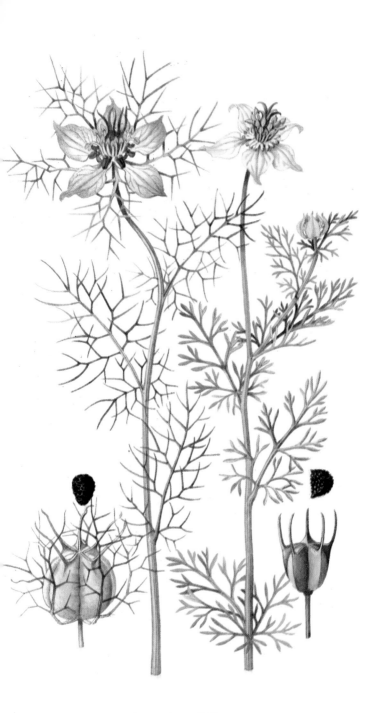

Love-in-a-Mist

PRICKLY RESTHARROW   *Ononis spinosa* L.

Family: Papilionaceae.

Description: The prickly restharrow has a strong taproot about 50 cm (20 in) long. This produces several strong thorny stems up to 60 cm (2 ft) high, ascending or upright, the lower part woody, which generally die back to the ground in winter. The foliage varies in shape and size. The loose, clustered, densely leaved inflorescences bear often short thorny shoots in the axils of their leaves, each with one to three flowers with strong pink corollas. It differs from other similar species found in Central Europe mainly by the shorter husk facing the calyx and the double row of hairs on its stem. (Other species are hairy all round).

Flowering time: Early summer to early autumn or fall.

Habitat: The plant likes to colonise chalky ground and poor meadows but can also be found on peaty soil, in light woodland and beside paths and fields. As cattle avoid prickly restharrow it spreads readily, particularly on meadows, and can be recognised from a distance by its bushy growth.

Distribution: The prickly restharrow grows over most of Europe apart from its most northerly areas and the high mountains. It spreads in the south to North Africa and in the east via Turkey to the Caucasus and Central Asia.

Parts used: Root (Radix Ononidis)

Harvesting time: Late summer to mid October.

Harvesting instructions: The roots are dug out or, because they are often firmly stuck in hard ground, levered out with a pickaxe. After removing all the earth and thoroughly cleaning them the harvested parts are threaded on a line to dry. The drug has an unpleasant, weak, sweetish smell and a harsh repulsive, slightly sweet and irritating taste with a scratchy aftertaste.

Ingredients: The drug contains up to 0.2 per cent ethereal oil. Other ingredients are the isoflavonglycoside ononin, triterpene, such as ononcol and the pterocarpanderivate trifolirhizin.

Uses: Experiments have proved that the drug has a diuretic effect, mild in contrast with juniper, and so it does not irritate the kidneys. It is assumed that other ingredients besides the ethereal oil and the flavonoids, are responsible for this effect.

Side effects: No side effects are known.

History: A southern type of prickly restharrow was used in antiquity but our drug has been in use since the sixteenth century. Flowering restharrow herbage was also used in folk medicine in the past.

Prickly Restharrow

MARJORAM   *Origanum vulgare* L.

Family: Labiatae.

Description: This robust perennial plant reaches a height of up to 50 cm (20 in) and survives the winter by means of its long thin rootstock. The mostly upright, red to brownish-red spreading stems are rather stout. The numerous oil glands give the plant a harsh, aromatic scent. Non-flowering side branches arise from the axils of the leaves at the base of the stem. Further up there are flowering side shoots, and right at the top umbel-like paniculate inflorescences. The short pedicellated flowers sit singly in the axils of often intense red-brown bracts. The four stamens with small violet anthers and the style with its split stigma protrude from the carmine-red to flesh-coloured corolla.

Flowering time: Mid-summer to early autumn or fall.

Habitat: Marjoram likes to colonise dry, warm places. It is found particularly on sunny chalky slopes but also in mountain meadows, in light woodland and on cleared land.

Distribution: The plant grows in Europe from the Mediterranean to Ireland and Scotland and in the north as far as Central Scandinavia. To the east it extends to Siberia, the Himalayas and Iran.

Parts used: Herbage (Herba Origani).

Harvesting time: Mid-summer to early autumn or fall.

Harvesting instructions: Marjoram herbage was collected and laid out to dry after the thicker parts of the stems had been removed. When they were being gathered, the stems had to be cut off so the taproot was not torn from the ground. The drug has a strong, pleasant, spicy fragrance similar to that of sweet marjoram and an aromatic, bitter, slightly harsh and salty taste.

Ingredients: The herbage contains tannin and bitter constituents, as well as up to 0.5 per cent ethereal oil with thymol and carvocrol as the main constituent, tannin.

Uses: The drug has an emetic and anti-convulsive effect and is used for complaints of the upper respiratory tracts and for convulsive and whooping coughs. Because of its bitter constituents it is also used for stomach upsets and loss of appetite. The drug is also said to have a choloretic effect.

Side effects: This drug has no known side effects.

History: The plant is an old medicine, but the herbage used in Greek medicine was probably a local species of marjoram. Dioscorides recommended it for poisonous animal bites and the Romans used it to drive away ants. Theophrastus also mentioned marjoram species as medicinal plants. During the Middle Ages it was not only a healing plant but also played a significant role in superstition.

Marjoram

PEONY

Paeonia officinalis L.

Family: Ranunculaceae.
Description: This perennial plant survives the winter by means of its turnip-like tuberous root. In spring several upright, sparsely branched herbaceous stems appear which form a plant about 50 cm (20 in) high. The alternate leaves are a shiny dark-green on top and light green and pilose underneath. The large flowers are carried singly at the ends of the stems. The wild form has five to eight usually dark red petals about 4—5 cm (1½—2 in) long. The cultivated forms in our gardens have many more petals because some of the numerous stamens found in the normal flowers have been changed into petals. The two or three ovaries with red stigmas develop into densely felted hairy follicles. This species differs from the large-leaved peony we cultivate by its more deeply incised leaves, which are entire in the former type.
Flowering time: Late spring to early summer.
Habitat: This plant prefers dry, chalky slopes. In Central Europe it is usually as a cultivated form in our gardens.
Distribution: The peony is a native of the greater part of Southern Europe, from Portugal to Albania and Turkey. Its northern limit reaches to the northern foothills of the Alps. It can alo be found in one area of Bohemia and on the sunny chalky hills of Thuringia, a remnant of former vineyards.
Parts used: Flowers (Flores Paeoniae).
Harvesting time: Late spring to early summer.
Harvesting instructions: The plucked red petals should be dried quickly so they do not fade. The drug must be protected from light when stored. When fresh it has a faint honey smell, lost when it is dried, and a harsh sweet taste with an astringent effect.
Ingredients: The flowers of the peony contain tannin and the colouring paeonin which consists of paeondin and glucose.
Uses: The drug is used to embellish cough mixtures and smokers' teas and has often been used to colour cough syrups. In the past the root was usually used for epileptic spasms.
Side effects: The flowers and seeds cause stomach and intestinal inflammation leading to vomiting, spasmodic pains and diarrhoea.
History: The peony is an old medicinal plant often prescribed by Greek doctors in antiquity. The drug was known to Hippocrates. The Roman doctor Galen used it and mentioned it in his writings.

Peony

RED POPPY   *Papaver rhoeas* L.

Family: Papaveraceae.
Description: The red poppy is usually an annual but occasionally biennial multi-stemmed 30−90 cm (12−35 in) high plant containing milky sap. The upright or ascending stems like the pinnate leaves are covered in bristly hairs. The flower buds hang down until the flowers unfurl. The long-stemmed flowers measure up to 10 cm (4 in) across. The bi-valve, bristly, hairy, green sepals fall off when the four fragile bright red, occasionally white or violet petals, open. The stamens carry blue-green anthers and surround the ovary in large numbers. The latter develops into a capsule with seven to nine transverse partitions inside and many dark brown, kidney-shaped seeds marked with a network of grooves.
Flowering time: Late spring to mid-summer.
Habitat: The poppy is a weed of cornfields, other fields, fallow land, and clearings in the lowlands and up into the alpine region.
Distribution: Originally only a native of the Mediterranean area, the plant can now be found throughout Europe apart from its far northern extremities as well as on the Atlantic Islands and from North Africa to temperate Asia. It was introduced into Atlantic and Pacific North America and also Australia and New Zealand.
Parts used: Flowers (Flores Rhoeados).
Harvesting time: Early to mid-summer.
Harvesting instructions: Only the petals were collected and quickly dried at a high temperature. The red colour changes to brown-violet. When fresh the drug has a weak narcotic smell but is odourless when dried. It has a weak bitter, slightly slimy taste.
Ingredients: The drug contains less than 0.1 per cent alkaloid; the main alkaloid is rhoeadin. Other constituents are anthocyan glycoside, mucilage and tannin; it does not contain opium alkaloids.
Uses: The flowers of the red poppy were once used against coughs and hoarseness. Nowadays they are sometimes scattered in cough medicines to colour them red.
Side effects: Though rhoeadin tends to produce spams its concentration in the drug is too small for it to have any poisonous effect.
History: Pliny and Theophrastus mentioned the flowers of various kinds of poppy, such as Papaver erraticum and P. argemone, which were added to food. Theophrastus also named a species called Papaver Rhoias, which probably signified our poppy. In the east this drug was often used as a cough mixture. It is not certain whether the flowers were used in Egyptian medicine or acts of worship. Remains of these plants were supposed to have been found in Egyptian graves.

Red Poppy

†OPIUM POPPY   *Papaver somniferum* L.

Family: Papaveraceae.
Description: The opium poppy's 30 to 150 cm (1–5 ft) high upright blue-green pruinose stem, branched at the top, rises from a spindle-shaped, branched root. Like the rest of the plant it is filled with a white milky sap. The tall, arched flower stalks carry only one flower, up to 10 cm (4 in) across which nods before it opens. The bristly hairy sepals that protect the bud soon fall off. The four petals are violet, white or red with a dark spot at the base. The numerous stamens have bluish-green anthers. The capsule which develops from the ovary contains many kidney-shaped, mostly blue-black finely pitted seeds. This species is very variable.
Flowering time: Summer.
Habitat: Opium poppies are cultivated as oil-producing and ornamental plants but have become naturalised on waste ground, by fences, footpaths and river embankments.
Distribution: The source plant of the opium poppy, cultivated since the Bronze Age, is a species of poppy from the Eastern Mediterranean (P. setigerum D.C.) which is still cultivated today along with the opium poppy in Northern France.
Parts used: Unripe fruit capsules (Fructus Papaveris immaturi); seeds (Semen Papaveris).
Harvesting time: Fruit capsules, mid-summer; seeds, late summer to early autumn or fall.
Harvesting instructions: The unripe fruit capsules were cut in half and, after the unripe seeds had been removed, quickly dried in gentle heat. The seeds were obtained from dried and ripened capsules, or from naturally ripe capsules. The narcotic smell and bitter taste of the fresh drug is lost after drying. The seeds are odourless and have a bitter oily taste.
Ingredients: Unripe poppy capsules contain approximately 0.2 per cent opium alkaloids and ripe capsules up to 0.4 per cent. The main alkaloid is morphine, other alkaloids are narcotine, codein, papaverin, thebain and narcein. The seeds contain approximately 50 per cent fatty oil, 20 per cent egg white, lecithine and some alkaloid traces, sugar, mucins, albumin, rubber and resins.
Uses: The importance of opium as a medicine has diminished in favour of the alkaloids isolated from it. Morphine is prescribed by doctors for unbearable pain, codeine and narcotin mainly as a cough mixture, and papaverin for cramp in the intestinal tract, gall-bladder and urinary passages. Opium is sometimes used for diarrhoea. An alkaloid-free oil is extracted from the seeds.
Toxic effect: Poppy capsules were once used as a sedative for coughs, insomnia and particularly for children. This dangerous practice sometimes resulted in fatal poisoning. Opium and morphine are addictive drugs and subject to the addictive drugs law.
History: The opium poppy has been used since the lake dwellings era. Opium has been used since the third century BC, morphine since 1804.

Opium Poppy

PARSLEY
Petroselinum crispum (MILL.) A. W. HILL

Family: Umbelliferae.

Description: Parsley is a biennial or perennial plant. In its first year it forms a basal leaf rosette which produces a leafy branched stem in its second year. The tripinnate leaves are shiny on top. Parsley has a strong characteristic smell which clearly distinguishes it from the similar but poisonous fool's parsley (Aethusa cynapium L.) whose flowers are pure white. The long-stemmed flower umbels consist of 10−20 rays each with its own small individual umbel. The insignificant petals are usually greenish-yellow, but sometimes have a reddish tint.

Flowering time: Early to mid-summer.

Habitat: This familiar aromatic plant can be found in nearly every kitchen garden but is also cultivated in fields and has become naturalised.

Distribution: It is assumed that parsley's homeland was the southern and western part of the Mediterranean. It is cultivated or naturalised over the whole of Europe up as far as Iceland, Norway and West Greenland, in North and South America, the West Indies, South Africa, India, Japan and Australia.

Parts used: Root (Radix Petroselini), fruit (Fructus Petroselini).

Harvesting time: Roots, early to mid-spring; fruit, late summer to early autumn or fall.

Harvesting instructions: The root was dug up, washed, split lengthwise and dried at temperatures up to 40°C. It has a distinctive aromatic smell and an initially sweet, but later bitter taste. To extract the fruits the umbels are cut off shortly before they ripen, bundled, and hung up to ripen. They smell spicy and have an aromatic burning taste.

Ingredients: The parsley roots contain approximately 0.2 per cent and the fruit 2−6 per cent ethereal oil with apiol and myristicin or allyltetramethoxybenzol as the main constituents with petroselenic acid.

Uses: The drug is a diuretic. Apiol acts as an excitant on the womb. The drug was occasionally used as a stomachic, a carminative or for menstrual complaints. The crushed fruits were formerly used against headlice and scabies mites.

Side effects: Poisoning by this plant is unheard of. The ethereal oil isolated from the fruit has a strong irritating effect on the intestines. An overdose of pure apiol causes miscarriages, and damages the kidneys, liver and heart.

History: Hippocrates and Dioscorides mention parsley and its effect in their writings. Charlemagne ordered its cultivation. The plant was also used in the Middle Ages for medicinal purposes. Parsley oil was first extracted by steam distillation in the fifteenth century.

Parsley

MASTERWORT
Peucedanum ostruthium (L.) KOCH

Family: Umbelliferae.

Description: Masterwort is a perennial plant that overwinters by means of its tuberous or top-shaped root which usually forms short subterranean stolons. The root, which produces a milky sap in spring, has many fibrous roots and is brown on the outside and white inside. It has a simple or only slightly branched, finely grooved, tubular stem, seldom exceeding 60 cm (2 ft in height. The basal foliage of the plant consists of simple or double three-part leaves i.e. the three petioled sections of the leaves are again in three or two parts. The umbels of white flowers, each consisting of 40–50 small umbels, are apical or axillary. As with all umbel flowers the five-part flowers have small white or reddish petals. The ovary develops into a yellowish white schizocarp. The whole plant has a strong herby smell.

Flowering time: Mid to late summer.

Habitat: Masterwort can be found in mountain meadows, fields, damp rubbish tips and on the banks of mountain streams in the Alps and alpine foothills from 1400 to 2700 m (4600–8800ft), but also now and again in the lower mountain ranges and lowlands where it has become naturalised from earlier cultivation.

Distribution: The original area of distribution was the Pyrenees and the Alps.

Parts used: Rootstock (Rhizoma Imperatoriae).

Harvesting time: Early to mid-spring and early to mid-autumn or fall.

Harvesting instructions: The rootstocks were dug up, freed from stolons and any remaining earth, then laid out or strung on a line to dry. Thicker roots were split lengthwise. The drug has an aromatic smell, and a biting taste with a spicy aromatic tang which stimulates the flow of saliva.

Ingredients: Masterwort contains 0.2–1.4 per cent ethereal oil, tannin, resin, palmitic acid, cumarinderivates, such as ostruthin, imperatorin and peucedanin.

Uses: The drug is no longer prescribed. Previously it was used mainly for loss of appetite, stomach and digestion disorders and as an additive to bitter liqueurs. This effect was based on its ethereal oil and bitter cumarin derivative content. Masterwort was also sometimes used as a diuretic, against gout and rheumatism.

Side effects: Cumarin derivatives are poisonous to fish. In exceptional circumstances masterwort can cause "meadow dermatitis".

History: Masterwort has certainly been used as a drug since the sixteenth century. At times it was prescribed as a cure-all and described in the Middle Ages as one of the most select herbs.

Masterwort

FRENCH BEAN   *Phaseolus vulgaris* L.

Family: Papilionaceae.

Description: When germinating the two greening cotyledons rise above the soil. The thin plant stem is 1−3 cm (½−1 in) long in the runner bean and 30−50 cm (12−20 in) high in the bush bean. The upright inflorescences bear opposite pairs of rather long-stemmed flowers in the axils of the subtending leaves. The corolla can be yellowish to greenish white, pink, red or violet. The straight or curved hanging pods, usually 10−20 cm (4−8 in) long, are generally greenish but can be yellowish-white to purple-violet. They contain up to eight bean seeds varying greatly in colour and size, and swell in a nodular manner.

Flowering time: Early summer to early autumn or fall.

Habitat: The bean is grown in gardens and fields.

Distribution: This bean's area of origin is probably the mountains of Central America. It is now cultivated everywhere.

Parts used: Pods (Fructus Phaseoli sine Semine).

Harvesting time: Late summer to mid-autumn or fall.

Harvesting instructions: The drug consists of the ripe pods without seeds and is obtainable when the beans are harvested. Any spotted or fungus-infected pods should be discarded. The pods are dried, first in the open air, then in temperatures between 30 and 50°C. The drug must have a white shiny appearance on the inside. It is odourless and has a weak slimy taste.

Ingredients: The pericarps contain betain trigonellin, biogene amines, such as asparigin and cholin, numerous amino acids such as arginin, tyrosin, leucin, lysin and tryptophan and also glucoki-ßine, traces of hydrocyanic acid, glycosides, silicic acids, vitamin and up to 50 per cent hemicellulose. The seeds and the unripe peicarps contain the toxalbumin, phasine, which is destroyed after boiling for 15 minutes.

Uses: The drug has diuretic properties and was used particularly for kidney and heart complaints, gout and rheumatism. It also has a slight sugar-reducing effect, which is why it is prescribed for mild forms of Diabetes Mellitus, to support the diet. It is not certain which of the ingredients produces this effect but it is unlike insulin.

Side effects: Fresh beans can produce skin irritation in sensitive people. This occurs in canning factories and is described as "bean scabies".

History: The garden bean originates in America. The plant was hardly known in Central Europe until the sixteenth century. The plant described by Hippocrates and mentioned by Theophrastus as "dolichos" was not the garden bean but a similar plant which grows in the Mediterranean area.

French Bean

NORWAY SPRUCE   *Picea abies* (L.) KARSTEN

Family: Pinaceae.

Description: This tree, whose trunk grows up to 2 m (6½ ftin diameter, usually reaches a height of 25–30 m (82–98 ft) in Central Europe. The straight trunk is regularly branched, tapers off towards the top and has a pointed crown. The bark of young trees is smooth but flakes off old trees in thin scales. The generally verticillate branches are horizontal or hang down slightly. Norway spruce is a shallow-rooted tree. The leaves (needles) are usually grooved on the underside. The male flowers stand erect when in full flower and are then reddish yellow. The whitish cone, an inflorescence, stands erect while in flower and is purplish red. Later the ripe, brown, hanging cone drops off completely. The seeds each have a light-brown wing by which they are carried far and wide.

Flowering time: Late spring.

Habitat: Norway spruce grows as a solitary tree or in extensive mixed forests.

Distribution: In Europe Norway spruce grows nearly to latitude 70 degrees north. In the east it reaches to the Volga, in the south to the Balkan mountains, and to the west the mountains of Eastern and Central France and the Pyrenees.

Use as a drug: The drug Resina Pini is extracted from the common spruce (Picea abies), the seaside pine tree (Pinus pinaster) and other related conifers, and consists of resin residues that have hardened in the air during extraction.

Extraction: The resin residues are scraped from the trees, which is why the resin is also referred to as scrape resin. The material collected is melted and cleaned, which can be carried out in several ways. German scrape resin is known as Gum Thus in England. In America it is called sarape, and in France galipot or barras, the latter referring to pieces collected from the ground. The drug consists of transparent yellowish pieces which are very brittle and sticky to the touch. They have a pleasant resiny smell and taste sharp, aromatic and bitter.

Ingredients: The resin consists mainly of abietin acid, pimar acid and ethereal oil.

Uses: The drug can be used for the manufacture of skin plasters and ointments. The resin is also used in the manufacture of putty and other products.

Side effects: No side effects are known.

History: Nothing is known about the application of the drug in earlier times. However, spruce needles were long used in folk medicine for respiratory troubles and as a bath additive.

Norway Spruce

ANISE   *Pimpinella anisum* L.

Family: Umbelliferae.
Description: This annual plant has a thin spindle-shaped root. The grooved stem can grow to a height of 50 cm (20 in), stands upright and is branched towards the top. The whole plant has the familiar anise smell. The lower leaves have long stems, but some of the upper leaves grow straight from their small basal sheath. The flowers grow at the ends of the main and side shoots in loose umbels each with some 7–15 principal rays. The calyx is no longer recognisable and the white petals have long sinuous tips. The double-seeded schizocarp is a long oval shape and greyish brown when ripe. The partial fruits are late to part from the plant and difficult to separate from each other.
Flowering time: Mid to late summer.
Habitat: The anise plant makes high demands on soil and weather, so it is only grown as a herb or medicinal plant in Central Europe, but it sometimes becomes naturalised for a time.
Distribution: Anise probably originates from the East and is cultivated mainly in Spain, Italy and Russia.
Parts used: Fruits (Fructus Anisi).
Harvesting time: Mid-summer to early autumn or fall.
Harvesting instructions: When the fruit begins to ripen the herbage is cut off and threshed which makes the fruit drop out. The drug has a spicy smell and a distinct, pleasant, spicy, sweet taste.
Ingredients: The anise fruit contains 2–6 per cent ethereal oil, olium anisi which consists of 90 per cent anethol, fatty oil and choline.
Uses: By reason of its ethereal oil content the drug has anti-spasmodic and carminative characteristics and acts as a discharging agent. It is also claimed that the drug increases the flow of milk and has an oestrogen effect, the latter attributed to the dianethol which occurs particularly in anise liquors and is similar to synthetic oestrogen. By stimulating the digestive glands and the peristaltic action of the stomach, the drug promotes the appetite and digestion. Its expectorant effects on coughing are attributed to the beneficial influence of the ethereal oil on the ciliated epithelium of the bronchi. The drug is also used as a culinary herb, and the ethereal oil for the extraction of the anethol. It is used externally against headlice and scabies mites.
Side effects: No side effects are known from using the fruits.
History: The Egyptians used the anise fruit as a spice. Dioscorides and Pliny reported the healing power of the drug. Charlemagne mentions it in his "Capitulare". In the sixteenth century the plant was extensively cultivated in Central Europe, and its ethereal oil was also mentioned for the first time.

214

Anise

BURNET SAXIFRAGE   *Pimpinella saxifraga* L.

Family: Umbelliferae.

Description: This plant survives by means of its spindle-shaped to cylindrical sparsely branched root, which contains a milky sap. It has a sharp goat-like smell. The slender tubular stem grows between 15 and 75 cm (6−30 in) high and is usually sparsely branched. It has well developed long-stemmed leaves at the base. The leaves' petioles get shorter towards the top. The apical umbels each consist of about 6 to 15 small umbels which hang down at first, then stand erect after flowering. The five petals, hairy on the outside, are mostly white or yellowish-white, occasionally pink to purple. As their long pointed tips are bent inwards they are an upside-down heart shape.

Flowering time: Mid-summer to early autumn or fall.

Habitat: Burnet saxifrage can be found on all types of soil particularly on chalky ground from the northern area to the Alps. It can be found on dry, barren meadows, heaths, fallow fields and sometimes on arable land. It is also grown in gardens as a decorative plant.

Distribution: This plant can be found throughout Europe to Western Siberia. It was introduced into North America.

Parts used: Root (Radix Pimpinellae).

Harvesting time: Early to mid-spring and early to mid-autumn or fall.

Harvesting instructions: The roots were carefully dug out and shaken free from the earth then thoroughly washed with water. But they must not stay in water for long. They are then threaded on a line and dried in artificial heat (up to 40°C). The drug has a spicy smell and an aromatic taste with a sharp, biting, aftertaste.

Ingredients: The drug radix pimpinellae which consists of the roots pimpinella saxifraga and p. magna, contains up to 0.4 per cent ethereal oil, and cumarinderivates such as pimpinelline, isopimpinelline, bergapten, isobergapten, umbelliferon, sphondin and peucedanin, and also saponins, tannin, resin and rubber.

Uses: The burnet saxifrage root has an expectorant effect and is used for complaints of the mouth and throat cavities. Apart from its use as a gargle it is sometimes used as a stomachic and in folk medicine as a diuretic and emmenagogue, for intestinal catarrh and also for slow healing wounds.

Side effects: No side effects of this drug are known.

History: Burnet saxifrage was not known in antiquity. Reliable information about its use can first be found in the eighth century. From the sixteenth century it has been a part of regular medical supplies. The root was also occasionally used as a pesticide.

Burnet Saxifrage

SCOTS PINE
MOUNTAIN PINE

Pinus sylvestris L.
Pinus mugo TURRA

Family: Pinaceae.

Description: Depending on location, soil and climate the Scots pine can reach a height of 20—40 m (56—130 ft). The bark on the lower part of the trunk, which is clear of branches, is dark brown to black and scaly, while on the upper part and the branches it is a foxy red. The blue-green needles are always borne in pairs. The male flowers are sulphur-yellow, the females develop into woody cones, whose seeds are winged. There are numerous varieties.

Flowering time: Scots pine, late spring; mountain pine, early summer to mid-summer.

Habitat: The Scots pine (Pinus sylvestris L.)is found particularly on sandy ground. The mountain pine (Pinus mugo TURRA) often forms extensive woods in the Alps, and also grows on high moorland and on the summits of low mountain ranges.

Distribution: The Scots pine can be found over most of Europe and Siberia, as far north as latitude 70° north.

Uses as medicine: Turpentine (terebinthina) is extracted from pines whose trunks have been deliberately wounded as a viscous resinous sap, which is then collected and cleaned. This is converted by steam distillation into 20—25 per cent turpentine oil (Oleum Terebinthinae) and 65—70 per cent colophonium as a distillation residue. The young shoots (Turiones Pini) collected in April and May and the pine needle oil extracted by steam distillation from the needles and shoot tips (Oleum Pini silvestris) as well as the dwarf-pine oil (Oleum Pini pumilionis) extracted from the mountain pine are used for medical purposes. The wood tar (Pix liquida) extracted from the wood of various types of pine by dry distillation is also used.

Ingredients: Turpentine contains resinol acids, terpene and resin, has a balsamic odour and tastes bitter. Turpentine oil, consisting of pines, has a resinaceous smell and a sharp taste; the resin colophonium on the other hand consists of resin acids. The pine shoots contain ethereal oil with pines, cadines, and sylvestrine, and bitter constituents, tannin and resin. The dwarf-pine oil contains pines, cadine, sylvestrine and phellandres. The wood tar contains benzol, toluol, phenol, cresol and brenzcatechin, also vitamin C when fresh.

Uses: Pine shoots like turpentine oil have a diuretic effect, but are only used externally because they severely irritate the kidneys. Shoots and pine needle oil are used in inhalants; pine needle oil and dwarf-pine oil as a linament. Turpentine oil and colophonium are used for skin plasters and ointments, and wood tar for dermatitis.

Side effects: When the drug is used in therapeutic doses no side effects are to be expected. But some 60 ml of turpentine oil can be fatal if taken internally.

History: Some of the drugs, such as colophonium and turpentine were used as medicines in antiquity.

Scots Pine   Mountain Pine

RIBWORT PLANTAIN   *Plantago lanceolata* L.

Family: Plantaginaceae.

Description: The perennial ribwort plantain has a short taproot set with many fibrous roots. The lanceolate leaves, up to 30 cm (12 in) long, form a basal rosette. The five-grooved leafless stem of the spiked inflorescence is a constant feature, while the leaves and inflorescence vary enormously in form and size. Each individual flower on the compact globular or short cylindrical flower spike stands in a small dry-skinned subtending leaf. The lowest flowers of each spike bloom first, the styles project and become capable of fertilisation. The four white to brownish petals are joined into a tube from which four stamens hang out wide apart during flowering. The fruits each containing two small seeds are tiny lid capsules.

Flowering time: Late spring to early autumn or fall.

Habitat: Ribwort plantain can be found in meadows, grassland, at the edges of woods and pathways and in arable fields, but it prefers drier locations than the greater plantain. It was also cultivated.

Distribution: Ribwort is found all over Europe and North and Central Asia. It was introduced by immigrants to North Africa, North and South America, Australia and New Zealand.

Parts used: Herbage (Herba Plantaginis lanceolatae).

Harvesting time: Late spring to early summer.

Harvesting instructions: Harvested material must be dried quickly at 50–60°C to prevent hydrolysis of the aucubin by an enzyme which is contained in the plant. Blackish-brown discoloured herbage is of no use. The drug is odourless and has a harsh, slightly salty and bitter taste.

Ingredients: The most important ingredient of the ribwort is the glycoside aucubin; it also contains tannin, mucilage, silicic acid and vitamin C, chlorogenic and ursolic acid and potassium.

Uses: The drug has anti-bacterial characteristics. These are attributed to the aglykon of the aucubin, aucubigenin, which is released by the beta-glucosidasen contained in the plant. Aucubin and the black-brown polymerisates of the aucubigenin are ineffectual. The drug has an enveloping and expectorant effect for infections of the upper respiratory tracts and the urinary system and is prescribed for stomach and intestinal diseases because of its tannin content. As it also has a coagulating effect it was used for the treatment of wounds.

Side effects: There are no known side effects.

History: Ribwort is an old healing plant which was described in detail by Dioscorides. It has been used both internally and externally. Species of plantain were described by Hieronymus Bock as the most useful of all herbs and used for many complaints.

Ribwort Plantain

GREATER PLANTAIN   *Plantago major* L.

Family: Plantaginaceae.
Description: The greater plantain is usually perennial and survives the winter by means of its short rootstock set with long fibrous roots. The five to seven-veined leaves are all arranged in a basal rosette that lies flat on the ground. Each plant grows long, upright or ascending flower stems carrying cylindrical spikes densely covered with flowers. The yellow anthers hang conspicuously from the small yellowish-green flowers to facilitate wind pollination. The style protrudes from the flower long before flowering to prevent self-pollination. The outer coat of the small seeds swells up and becomes sticky when moistened, so they are readily distributed by man and animal. The hoary plantain (P. media L.) in contrast to the greater plantain has sessile or short-stemmed leaves and a flower stem much longer than the spike.
Flowering time: Early summer to mid-autumn or fall.
Habitat: The plant usually grows near human habitation or activities, such as along roads and footpaths, on village greens and pastures.
Distribution: From Europe and North and Central Asia the greater plantain was exported all over the world.
Parts used: Herbage (Herba Plantaginis majoris).
Harvesting time: Late spring to mid-summer.
Harvesting instructions: The herbage of the greater plantain must not be crushed when harvested and should be dried immediately in thin layers at between 50−60°C. Parts that have turned black-brown should be discarded. The drug is no longer used medicinally since the demand can quite easily be met by ribwort plantain which has a much higher content of aucubin. The drug is odourless and has a bitter, slightly salty taste.
Ingredients: Like the ribwort the greater plantain contains aucubin, tannin, and 0.2 per cent ethereal oil.
Uses: Greater plantain herbage was used in the same way as that of Plantago lanceolata. The fresh leaves were used in the past for healing wounds and ulcers, as the juice from the leaves has an anti-inflammatory, cleansing and skin-forming effect.
Side effects: This drug has no side effects.
History: The various types of plantain are among the oldest medicinal plants. Dioscorides and Celsus praised their cooling, resolving and astringent characteristics for healing wounds. In the Middle Ages species of plantain were among the most frequently used healing plants.

Greater Plantain

BITTER MILKWORT

Polygala amara L.

Family: Polygalaceae.
Description: This 5 to 15 cm (2−6 in) high perennial plant has a spindle-shaped, many-branched root which produces many upright or ascending stems. The stem leaves are usually widest in the middle and pointed. The leaves at the base of the plant form a rosette. All the leaves have a bitter taste. The flowers are congregated in a pyramid-shaped, partly tufted inflorescence, very close together at first but later more loosely arranged as the axis stretches. The colour of the flowers varies considerably and can be blue, violet, red or white. The corolla is about 3−6 mm long. It consists of a 4 to 6.5 mm long wing and a carina which is constricted in front of the slightly fringed appendix. The fruit capsule inside the carina is up to 6 mm long.
Flowering time: Late spring to early summer.
Habitat: Bitter milkwort grows on rocky turf, in meadows watered by springs and dryish turf on chalk.
Distribution: There is insufficient knowledge about the habitat of bitter milkwort.
Parts used: Herbage (Herba Polygalae amarae).
Harvesting time: Late spring to early summer.
Harvesting instructions: Bitter milkwort herbage is collected while in flower from dry places complete with roots. Plants growing in damp soil contain hardly any bitter constituents. The parts used are dried in a well ventilated and shady area. The drug is odourless and has a very bitter taste. Material that tastes only slightly bitter should be discarded.
Ingredients: The drug contains saponin, bitter constituents, the phenolglycoside gaultherin, tannin and rubber.
Uses: The plant is used primarily as a discharging agent, the effect being attributed to the saponines as well as the gaultherin and its aglycon. Due to its bitter constituents it is used as an appetite stimulant and a stomachic. The Greek name Polygala means 'plenty of milk' and explains its use as a galactogogue. This effect is said to be caused by the saponines.
Side effects: No known side effects are known from using this drug.
History: The bitter milkwort was relatively late to be included in the medical treasury. After the effective characteristics of the exotic drug Radix Senegae, from the senega root of the same plant family, were discovered in the eighteenth century, more attention was given to the native polygala species.

Bitter Milkwort

KNOTGRASS
Polygonum aviculare L.

Family: Polygonaceae.

Description: Knotgrass is a generally prostrate, occasionally climbing, bluish-green, partly purple-red tinted herb. The root, spindle-shaped at the top and branched at the bottom, produces several many-branched, jointed stems that usually spread in every direction. These are set with leaves at the nodes right up to the tip. The small 2−3 mm long, short-stemmed flowers form two to five-flowered clusters in the axils. The greenish-white to pink-red flower sheath is in five parts with a funnel-shaped base. The ovary develops into a triangular, blackish purple nut. The plant varies greatly in external appearance and leaf shape according to its location, which is why many varieties are distinguishable.

Flowering time: Late spring to late autumn or fall.

Habitat: The knotgrass is possibly the commonest species of Polygonaceae in Central Europe. It grows in the plain and up into the Alpine region and likes to grow near human settlements, as well as on arable fields, banks between fields and poor grassy areas.

Distribution: Knotgrass can be found over most of the world and is absent only from Tropical Africa, South Africa, India and Polynesia.

Parts used: Flowering herbage (Herba Polygoni avicularis).

Harvesting time: Early summer to early autumn or fall.

Harvesting instructions: Dusty specimens should not be collected and while drying the colour must not change. Roots and bad parts of the plant should be removed. The drug is nearly odourless and has a slightly astringent taste.

Ingredients: The herbage of the knotgrass contains 0.2 per cent water soluble and 1 per cent water insoluble silicic acid, approximately 3−4 per cent tannin, flavonoid, phenol-carbon acid and mucilage.

Uses: The drug has a slight astringent, diuretic, capillary sealing and vasoconstrictive effect. Accordingly it is used as a diuretic for gall-bladder and kidney problems and for rheumatic complaints. It is also used as a supporting agent for treatment of tuberculosis of the lungs.

Side effects: As its effect is only weak no side effects are to be expected.

History: In ancient Greece and the Middle Ages the drug was used for haemoptysis, diarrheoa and kidney complaints. In the last century it was misused as a wonder drug against tuberculosis of the lungs.

Knotgrass

COMMON POLYPODY   *Polypodium vulgare* L.

Family: Polypodiaceae.
Description: The rhizome of this fern creeps just below or above the surface of the ground and is covered in brown, chaffy hairs. Single upright 50 cm (20 in)high leaves (fronds) spring from the rhizome. The young leaves are longitudinally rolled up, and the older ones carry at least in the upper part many round, brown spots (sori) underneath. These are catapulted from their containers during dry weather by a special mechanism and spread about by the wind. When these tiny spores germinate, they first grow into rootless, flat, heart-shaped prothalli only a few millimetres across on whose underside the sex organs are developing. New fern plants develop from fertilised egg cells produced during the sexual phase of reproduction.
Spores ripen: Late summer to early autumn or fall.
Habitat: Common polypody is found on shady slopes, rocks or walls and on forest soil. It grows mostly on primitive rock or sandy soil, less frequently where the subsoil is chalky.
Distribution: Common polypody can be found throughout the north temperate zone, in America as far south as Mexico, and in South Africa. In Central Europe it can be found particularly plentifully in hilly areas and grows in alpine regions up to 2200 m (7200 ft).
Parts used: Rhizome (Rhizoma Polypodii).
Harvesting time: March to April and September to October.
Harvesting instructions: The rhizome is freed from roots, remains of fronds and chaffy scales before it is dried. The useful material is threaded on a line to dry and hung in a well ventilated, shady place. The drug must be dried properly. It smells slightly of rancid oil and tastes sweet but later slightly bitter and rough.
Ingredients: The rhizome of the common polypody contains tannin, saponins, including the sweet tasting osladin, resin and mucilage.
Uses: The drug was formerly used as an expectorant and discharging agent for respiratory complaints and as a mild laxative. Common polypody is used in the liquor industry in the manufacture of bitter liqueurs.
Side effects: There are no known side effects.
History: This plant was first mentioned by Theophrastus, an Aristotelian scholar who produced a multi-volume botanical book in the third century BC. The common polypody is also listed in Dioscorides' book "Pharmacology", the most important publication of antiquity dealing with the healing powers of plants. The herbals of the sixteenth century also report in detail about the common polypody.

Common Polypody

BLACK POPLAR   *Populus nigra L.*

Family: Salicaceae.
Description: The black poplar is a slim 30 m (98 ft) high tree of pyramidal growth. The trunk can reach over 2 m (6½ ft) across. The initially greyish white bark soon changes into a blackish bark (hence the name black poplar) with deep cracks. The pointed buds with four to six sticky scales have a pleasant smell before flowering. The male flowers, whose stamens have purplish red anthers, form cylindrical catkins up to 9 cm (3½ in) long, the females into slimmer catkins which lengthen once they have been fertilised. The seeds are covered in a downy coat of fine white hairs by means of which they are dispersed over a wide area. The balsam poplar (P. balsamifera L.) also used medicinally, has short thick branches and usually large buds, whose balsam scent can be smelled from quite a distance.
Flowering time: Mid-spring.
Habitat: The black poplar prefers well lit places. From time to time it can be found in larger numbers along rivers, in riverside thickets and meadow woods. This tree is often planted to form avenues.
Distribution: The origin of the black poplar is difficult to establish definitely as it has been planted all over Central Europe.
Parts used: Winter buds (Gemmae Populi).
Harvesting time: Mid-spring.
Harvesting instructions: The poplar buds are harvested while still closed. After thorough drying they must be stored in airtight containers. The drug has a pleasant balsamic smell and an aromatic bitter taste. Gemmae Populi is derived from Populus nigra, P. balsamifera and various other species.
Ingredients: Poplar buds contain 0.5 per cent of pleasant chamomile-like smelling ethereal oil with caryophils as the main constituent. Other constituents are the phenolglycoside salicin and populin and also flavonoids, tannin and resin.
Uses: The glycoside complex is said to reduce the uric acid in the blood and increase the passing of uric acid. Therefore the drug was used for articular rheumatism (polyarthritis), and for disorders of the urinary organs and externally as poplar ointment for burns, haemorrhoids, wounds and inflammations.
Side effects: This drug has no known side effects.
History: Poplar buds produce a drug which was used in every era though only to a modest extent. In the Middle Ages poplar ointment was known by the name populeon.

Black Poplar

SILVERWEED

Potentilla anserina L.

Family: Rosaceae.

Description: Silverweed is a herbaceous plant that reaches a height of over 8 cm (3 in). It survives from year to year by means of its thick branched rootstock, covered on the upper side with the remains of dead bracts and leaf stalks. In spring it develops its characteristic interrupted pinnate leaves, covered at first on both sides but later only on the underside with silver hairs. These are initially all radical. Later stolons emerge from the axils of these basal leaves, and form leaf rosettes and roots at their nodes. Because of this vegetative reproduction by stolons silverweed usually forms dense colonies. The flowers are borne singly (rarely in pairs) on long stems which emerge from the nodes of the stolons and are up to 2 cm (½ in) wide. The petals are golden yellow.

Flowering time: Late spring to late summer.

Habitat: This plant is plentiful almost everywhere, but prefers fertile or salty soil and is often found on village greens and in meadows.

Distribution: Silverweed grows over almost the whole Northern Hemisphere. In Europe it is missing only from southern parts. In the south-east its distribution reaches the Caucasus, Lebanon and the Himalayas.

Parts used: Herbage (Herba Anserinae).

Harvesting time: Late spring to late summer.

Harvesting instructions: The silverweed is harvested shortly before and while it is in flower and dried in a well ventilated shady place. The drug is odourless and has a harsh astringent taste.

Ingredients: The plant contains mainly tannin, and also flavonoids, resin and mucilage, organic acids, stearins and choline.

Uses: Due to its tannin contents the drug is used for intestinal catarrh and as an anti-spasmodic agent for menstrual complaints and intestinal colic. Externally it is used as a gargle for inflammatory illnesses, and for wounds, ulcers and rashes.

Side effects: This drug has no known side effects.

History: This drug was not known to medicine in antiquity since the plant does not grow in the Mediterranean countries. However, it was highly valued by Germanic medicine. The herbals of the Middle Ages also praise the healing powers of silverweed.

Silverweed

COMMON TORMENTIL
Potentilla erecta (L.) RAUSCHEL

Family: Rosaceae.

Description: This perennial plant up to 50 cm (20 in) high survives winter by means of a finger-thick, blackish brown rootstock which is yellowish-red when freshly cut but blood-red when old. Usually several stems arise from a two or more-forked branched rootstock which on robust plants are generally arranged in a circle. The outer stems are decumbent, those further in ascending and the innermost erect. The usually four-lobed yellow flowers, about 10 mm wide, slightly darker at the base, grow on long, thin, softly hairy stems. Since the plant is polymorphic several varieties and forms are distinguished.

Flowering time: Summer.

Habitat: This generally distributed plant grows from the lowlands up into the alpine foothills at over 2000 m (6540 ft).

Distribution: Common tormentil is well established throughout Europe from the Azores and Shetland Islands in the west to Northern Scandinavia in the north and in the south from Portugal via Central Spain and Italy to the Balkan Peninsula. Further east it can be found from the Caucasus and the Urals to Asia.

Parts used: Rootstock (Rhizoma Tormentillae).

Harvesting time: Early to mid-spring and early to mid-autumn or fall.

Harvesting instructions: The tormentil's rootstock can generally be easily lifted out of the ground as the plants prefer loose soil. After any clinging parts have been removed they are washed and laid out in a thin layer for the first stage of drying or threaded on a string. Drying is then completed in gentle artificial heat. The drug is odourless and has a harsh astringent taste.

Ingredients: The rhizomes of the bloodwort contain 20 per cent tannin, tormentil, tormentol, and also organic acids, resin and rubber.

Uses: Due to its high tannin content the drug is used for stomach and intestinal catarrh as well as mouthwashes for inflammation of the throat and mouth cavity. It is used industrially as tannin and in the manufacture of ink.

Side effects: This drug has no known side effects.

History: Common tormentil was used as a medicinal plant in antiquity. The Hippocratians were familiar with its effects. It was often prescribed in the Middle Ages but was later forgotten with the arrival of the ratanhia root. When during the World War 1 this drug was no longer available people recalled the tormentil.

Common Tormentil

Family: Primulaceae.
Description: The oxlip overwinters by means of its strong root-stock which produces a rosette of basal leaves in spring. The margins of the young, hairy leaves in particular distinctly curve in towards the underside. The wrinkly leaf surface merges into the broad winged stem. Numerous ½ to2 cm (⅛–½ in) long, pedicellated flowers are clustered in an umbel which faces to one side and is carried on a tall leafless stalk. Each flower is surrounded by a five-tipped calyx. The corolla is sulphur-yellow with a greenish-yellow to light orange central ring.
Flowering time: Spring.
Habitat: The oxlip grows in meadows, thickets and meadow woods, from the lowlands to alpine foothills and prefers hilly areas.
Distribution: The oxlip is distributed throughout Central Europe to the Ukraine and from there to the Urals and via the Caucasus to Armenia and Northern Iran to the Altai Mountains.
Parts used: Root (Radix Primulae).
Harvesting time: Mid-autumn or fall.
Harvesting instructions: The rootstocks are dug out and washed clean of any remaining soil. The useful material is then dried in the air and finished off with artificial heat. The drug Radix Primulae consists of roots of the oxlip and the cowslip. The dried root of the oxlip smells of anise. It tastes bitter and rough.
Ingredients: The drug contains up to 10 per cent saponins, the content of which is highest at the beginning of the flowering time and in the first winter month. Main saponins are the primula and the elatior acid. Other constituents are ethereal oil and silicic acid. It is debatable whether the phenolglycosides, primverosid and primulaverosid, are present in the plant.
Uses: The oxlip is used primarily for its saponine content as an expectorant and discharging agent for complaints of the respiratory tract.
Side effects: Large doses of the drug cause vomiting and diarrhoea, but poisoning is unknown.
History: The root was used in the early Middle Ages. First accurate details are contained in sixteenth century herbals. It was later replaced by the exotic drug "Radix Senegae" and forgotten. Since the World War 1 when the senega root was no longer available it has received equal status with it as "Radix Senegae germanicae".

Oxlip

*COWSLIP   *Primula veris* L.

Family: Primulaceae.

Description: The cowslip survives from year to year by means of its rootstock. Its leaves form a rosette at its upper end and are rolled backwards when young. The leaves are about 6 cm (2½ in) long at flowering time and later become bigger. The whole plant is densely hairy. The flowers are normally arranged in a one-sided umbel on a stem up to 30 cm (1 ft) tall. The flowers are usually more or less nodding and grow from the axils of linear bracts on 1–2 cm (¼–½ in) pedicels. The bell-shaped five-sided calyx is light green to greenish-yellow, and has a pleasa corolla tube can be longer or shorter than the calyx and is marked with five orange spots. The fruit consists of a capsule up to 1 cm (¼ in) long which has an opening lid and contains warty seeds.

Flowering time: Mid to late spring.

Habitat: The cowslip likes chalky soil and can be found on arid turf, in dry meadows, on slopes and in dry mixed woods.

Distribution: The plant is at home over most of Central Europe and grows in the whole of Central Asia and the Near East with the exception of the northernmost areas and northern East Asia (the Amur area).

Parts used: Root (Radix Primulae); flowers (Flores Primulae).

Harvesting time: Root, mid-autumn or fall; flowers mid to late spring.

Harvesting instructions: The root is dug out, dried freely in the air and nished off by artificial heat. The drug has an anise smell and tastes bitter and rough. The flowers are gathered with their calyces and any flowers that have already wilted must be removed. When fresh the drug has a pleasant smell which gets weaker during drying and has a sweet, slightly slimy taste.

Ingredients: The main ingredient of the root is saponin, and the phenolglycosides primverosid and primulaverosid. They are split by the enzyme primverase which is responsible for the characteristic smell. Other ingredients are ethereal oil and silicic acid. The flowers contain in the calyx saponin, as well as ethereal oil and resin.

Uses: The root forms, with those of the oxlip, the drug Radix Primulae. As a decoction it is used as an expectorant and discharging agent. The flowers are less effective.

Side effects: An overdose can lead to vomiting and diarrhoea.

History: The roots of the cowslip, whose effects were described in detail during the sixteenth century, were increasingly replaced by the senega root after World War I.

Cowslip

SLOE, BLACKTHORN   *Prunus spinosa* L.

Family: Rosaceae.

Description: The sloe is a squarrose, densely branched shrub or a low tree which grows 1 to 2 m (3−6½ ft) high. As its widely creeping roots produce leafy shoots it is often found in dense hedgerows. The young branches often grow thorns later. The flowers are borne singly on short shoots. They appear in large numbers usually before the leaves. The brilliant white, softly scented petals attract insects. The anthers are yellow or reddish. The ovary develops into a globular fruit, green at first, then blue-black when ripe and generally covered in bloom. It contains a stone from which the sour-tasting green flesh separates after the frost.

Flowering time: Mid to late spring.

Habitat: The sloe colonises dry, sunny areas. It is commonly found throughout Central Europe but less frequent further north. It often grows in hedges together with dog roses, blackberries and other thorny bushes.

Distribution: Prehistoric finds indicate that the sloe was at the latest at home in the Early Stone Age in Central Europe as many sloe stones were found dating back to that time in Swiss lake dwellings. In Europe the distribution extends in the north to Scotland and Southern Scandinavia and in the east to the Urals. It can also be found in the Near East, North Africa and North America.

Parts used: Flowers (Flores Pruni spinosae).

Harvesting time: Mid to late spring.

Harvesting instructions: Sloe flowers should be collected in dry weather before the leaves appear. They must not be turned during the drying. The colour of the dried drug is said to be ivory. Brownish coloured flowers and any attacked by insects must be discarded. When fresh they have a sweet and weak bitter-almond smell and a bitter taste. The smell is lost when they are dried.

Ingredients: Sloe flowers contain as effective constituents flavonoids, mainly camphorol-glycosides and quercetin, quercitrin, rutin, hyperosid and traces of hydrogen cyanide glycosides.

Uses: The drug is used as a diuretic and mild laxative.

Side effects: There are no side effects.

History: The sloe was already in use in the lake dwelling era. Arabs, Greeks and Romans used the flowers for healing purposes, as they were also used in the Middle Ages.

240

Sloe Blackthorn

LUNGWORT   *Pulmonaria officinalis* L.

Family: Boraginaceae.

Description: Lungwort overwinters by means of its thin, branched rootstock, which almost simultaneously produces flower shoots and leaf rosettes. The 20 cm (8 in) high shoots are hairy like the leaves and the short pedicels. Apart from leaves the stem bears many-flowered inflorescence formed of several double cymes. The corolla is at first pink or red but becomes blue-violet with the alteration in its acid level. Like the calyx it grows together into a tube which opens up into a funnel shape and ends in five petal lobes.

Flowering time: Spring.

Habitat: Lungwort can be found in soil poor or rich in chalk, in light but not too dry deciduous woodland. It is particularly abundant in the lightly shaded valleys of small streams, but rarely grows under conifers.

Distribution: The plant grows over most of Europe. Its northern boundary runs through Southern Scandinavia (this species is missing in Norway), Southern Finland and the Central part of European Russia. In the east the lungwort reaches the Caucasus, and in the south the northern Balkan countries.

Parts used: Herbage (Herba Pulmonariae).

Harvesting time: Early spring to early summer.

Harvesting instructions: The aerial parts of the plant are gathered and well dried in the shade. The drug is odourless and has a slimy, slightly harsh, astringent taste.

Ingredients: The main ingredients contained in the lungwort are mucilage, tannin, saponins, water soluble and non soluble silicic acid and allantoin, glycosides, quercetin and kampferol and vitamin C. The silicic acid content increases continuously and reaches the highest point in autumn. The plant can be enriched with iron, phosphor, mangan and copper.

Uses: Lungwort is a drug used in the so-called folk medicine. It is used for illnesses of the respiratory organs because of the soothing and discharging effect of its saponins. Its reputed effect on tuberculosis of the lungs, for which it was once used, can be attributed to its soluble silicic acid content.

Side effects: No side effects are known.

History: Lungwort was unknown to medicine in antiquity. The healing powers of the plant were first noticed in the Middle Ages. It was illustrated in a herbal for the first time in 1583. Paracelsus (1493-1541) valued lungwort for its beneficial effects on illnesses of the respiratory tract.

Lungwort

†PASQUE FLOWER   *Pulsatilla vulgaris* MILL.

***Family:** Ranunculaceae.

Description: This plant survives the winter by means of its robust, often several-headed rootstock, which produces a tuft of leaves or an aerial shoot up to 10 cm (4 in) long in spring. The leaves at the base of these shoots first appear at flowering time. About 1–2 cm (¼–½ in) beneath the flower there is a whorl of three silver-haired bracts which grow together to sheath the stem. At the end of the shoot is an upright or slightly inclined flower whose five dark to light violet, ovate petals nod together to form a bell. The many carpels with long violet scars develop into single-seeded nutserving as a parachute. The pedicels which grow up to 40 cm (15 in) after flowering give the fruits a distinct tufted appearance. The whole plant is thickly hairy to start with.

Flowering time: Mid to late spring.

Habitat: The pasque flower likes warm, chalky localities such as sunny hillsides, stony slopes, heathland pastures and light, dry pinewoods.

Distribution: The pasque flower can be found in Northern, Central and Southern Europe.

Parts used: Herbage (Herba Pulsatillae).

Harvesting time: Late spring to mid-summer.

Harvesting instructions: The drug Herba Pulsatillae consists of the aerial parts of cultivated pasque flowers (P. vulgaris and P. pratensis, the meadow pasque flower) cut off as flowering finishes. Only the fresh drug and the extracts manufactured from it are effective.

Beware! All parts of the fresh plant are poisonous!

Ingredients: The herbage of the common pasque flower contains, apart from saponins and tannin, mainly the protoanemonin formerly called pulsatillacamphor which changes to the less effective anemonin when the plant is dried. This again transforms into the ineffective anemonin acid.

Uses: Only extracts from the fresh drug containing the effective ingredient anemonin were used in homeopathy for menstrual complaints, migraine, depressions and skin diseases.

Toxic effects: Protoanemonin has an extraordinarily irritating effect. It can produce redness of the skin, swelling, blisters and ulcerous disintegration, and its vapours can cause conjunctivitis and colds. Taken internally it produces vomiting, intestinal colic, diarrhoea and after reabsorption excitement, then paralysis of the central nervous system. Thirty plants lead to death by stopping the breathing.

History: The plants were used by the Celts.

Pasque Flower

PEDUNCULATE OAK   *Quercus robur* L.

Family: Fagaceae.
Description: The pedunculate oak, which grows over 50 m (163 ft) high has a massive irregular, many branched crown. Apart from strong lateral roots, the tree has a shorter, stronger taproot. The trunk can reach a diameter of 150 cm (5 ft) and its bark later becomes ash grey or blackish and deeply fissured. The alternate, short-stemmed leaves, shiny on top, matt to blue-green underneath, are covered in silky hair when young. The small awl-like stipules drop off early. The diclinous flowers appear while the leaves are developing. The male flowers stand in loosely arranged, 2−4 cm (½-1½ in) long pendulous catkins, the females singly or in twos to fives on common stalks which are longer than the petioles. The up to 3 cm (1 in) long fruit (acorn) sits in a cup. The durmast oak (Quercus petraea MATUSCHKA LIEBL.) usually has a slimmer trunk than the pedunculate oak and a regular crown. The petioles are longer than the female flowers.
Flowering time: Late spring.
Habitat: Both types of oak are generally scattered in deciduous and coniferous woodlands. The pedunculate oak sometimes forms small woods.
Distribution: Both oaks are found over most of Europe. In the east it reaches the Perm area (Siberia), the Caucasus countries Turkey. Its southern limit lies in North Africa.
Parts used: Bark (Cortex Quercus), fruits (Semen Quercus).
Harvesting time: Bark, early to mid-spring; fruits, mid-autumn or fall.
Harvesting instructions: Bark up to 4 mm thick is collected from small trees or 10 year old branches of the pedunculate oak or the durmast oak and dried before the leaves develop. The drug is odourless and has a very strong astringent taste, slimy in young bark, bitter in older bark. Acorns are odourless but have an astringent sweetish, harsh taste.
Ingredients: The oak rind contains 8−20 per cent tannin, which reduces during storage. The acorns contain quercite (sugar) tannin and albumin.
Uses: Oak bark is among the most effective tannin drugs. It is used only externally as an astringent agent. As a decoction it is used for compresses and baths for frostbite, sweaty feet, bleeding haemorrhoids and for painting bleeding and inflammed gums and other such conditions.
Side effects: If used internally it can lead to disorders of the intestinal tracts due to albumen precipitation (tanning).
History: The Hippocratians and Dioscorides praised the bark's astringent effect for intestinal colic. During the Middle Ages it was mainly the acorns that were used.

Pedunculate Oak

BUCKTHORN   *Rhamnus cathartica* L.

Family: Rhamnaceae.

Description: This roughly 3 m (10 ft) high shrub can also develop into a small tree, up to 8 m (26 ft) high. Its wood is very hard. The branches are often nearly opposite each other and mostly spreading with shiny ash-grey bark occasionally with small raised nodulesn terminate in a thorn. The opposite leaves vary greatly in shape from rounded and elliptical to oval. The pleasant-smelling flowers appear singly or several together in the leaf axils and form cymes. The petals of the inconspicuous flowers are whitish yellow. The pea-sized fruits are green at first, but black when ripe, rarely yellow, and have a bitter taste.

Flowering time: Late spring to early summer.

Habitat: The buckthorn can be found mainly on chalky soils, particularly in sunny, stony, dry places, on southerly and westerly slopes, and occasionally in woodland. It is less frequently found on gravelly and boggy ground.

Distribution: The shrub can be found over most of Europe, in the north to about 61° north. In the south it extends to Central Spain, Sicily, Macedonia, Algeria and eastwards to the Altai mountains.

Parts used: Fruits (Fructus Rhamni catharticae).

Harvesting time: Early to mid-autumn or fall.

Harvesting instructions: Buckthorn fruits are gathered when ripe and almost black. The gathered fruit is thoroughly dried in artificial heat. The drug has an unpleasant smell and an initially sweet but later bitter taste. The saliva turns greenish-yellow when the fruits are chewed.

Ingredients: The drug contains free and glycosidically bound anthrachinons as well as flavonoid glycosides.

Uses: The drug is particularly used in paediatrics as a mild laxative.

Side effects: About 20 unripe berries are said to cause violent vomiting, diarrhoea and kidney irritation, especially in children.

History: The drug was unknown to medicine in antiquity. However, it is assumed that it was already used in Nordic countries for medicinal purposes at this time. The herbals of the Middle Ages mention it only as a colouring agent. The "sap-green" made from unripe fruits was of great importance. In an alkaline medium it produces a yellow dye, in an acid medium a red dye.

Buckthorn

BLACKCURRANT   *Ribes nigrum* L.

Family: Grossulariaceae.

Description: The blackcurrant is a strong-growing shrub up to 2 m (6½ ft) high, whose young branches had light-coloured bark with hairs. The alternate, petioled leaves are glabrous on the upper surface and have many yellowish glands underneath. The flowers are arranged in many-flowered clusters which grow from the leaf axils. Each individual flower stands in an axil of a lanceolate, hairy bract. The majority of the hanging flowers pollinate themselves when the pollen falls from the anthers onto the arched edge of the stigma. The ovary develops into a many-seeded black berry with an aromatic taste.

Flowering time: Mid to late spring.

Habitat: The plant grows wild mainly in damp places such as wooded meadows, riverside thickets, flat bogland and occasionally goes wild from cultivation.

Distribution: The blackcurrant was probably at home originally only in northern Central Europe. This was confirmed by fossil finds in Southern Sweden. From here its distribution extends across the Caucasus, Siberia and the Himalayas to Manchuria. The shrub was then introduced into Central and South-East Europe. In Southern Europe it grows only as a cultivated plant.

Parts used: Leaves (Folia Ribis nigri).

Harvesting time: Late spring to early summer.

Harvesting instructions: Only a few leaves are taken from each branch when harvesting so that enough are left on the plant. The drug has to be dried carefully. It has a slight aromatic smell, and a harsh acidic and astringent taste.

Ingredients: The leaves of the blackcurrent contain tannin, organic acids and vitamin C. The fruit contains vitamin C, pigments, potassium, rutin, pectin and sugar.

Uses: The plant is a mild diuretic and sudorific but is hardly used nowadays. It is more commonly used as an ingredient of breakfast teas. Blackcurrant fruits, along with rose hips and sea buckthorn berries have the highest vitamin C content of any drug.

Side effects: This drug has no known side effects.

History: Currants were unknown to medicine in antiquity. In the sixteenth century the redcurrant was known as a medicinal plant. The blackcurrant was only occasionally mentioned and first appeared in the medical treasury in the eighteenth century. It is one of the medicines used in the Kneipp method. The blackcurrant has been cultivated since the middle of the eighteenth century.

Blackcurrant

DOG ROSE   *Rosa canina* L.

Family: Rosaceae.
Description: The dog rose is a vigorous 150 cm(5 ft) high shrub which can sometimes reach a height of several metres. Its long branches and twigs arch upwards and sideways and like its main stem, bear backward bent spines (wrongly called thorns). The rather thin leaves are imparipinnate. The pleasant smelling flowers are borne singly or several in a corymb on 2 cm (½ in) long petioles at the base of which there is a bract. The sepals bend backwards after flowering. The cordate petals are usually light pink, occasionally white. The receptacle of the flower develops into the well-known hip, a scarlet-red false fruit or berry which has many small hard fruits inside, hidden among hairs that can cause itching. There are different varieties and forms.
Flowering time: Early summer.
Habitat: The shrub can be found almost everywhere beside footpaths and along field boundaries, on barren meadows, light thickets and boundaries of woodlands particularly in hills and mountains (seldom above 1300 m/4300 ft).
Distribution: The dog rose can be found over most of Europe, West and Northern Asia and North America. Its northern limit in Europe stretches from the Orkneys across Southern Scandinavia to Southern Finland.
Harvesting time: Mid-autumn or fall.
Harvesting instructions: Rose hips are harvested as they start to ripen when they are still firm and have a deep red colour. The stems and remains of the calyces are cut off. The drug is pre-dried at 75−80°C for 30 minutes, then dried at 40−45°C. It is almost odourless. Rose hips are harvested mainly from wild growing plants. The flesh of the fruit has a sweet-sour astringend the individual fruit tastes aromatic.
Ingredients: The pericarps contain a considerable amount of vitamin C, further vitamins B & K, sugar, organic acids, pectin, tannin, flavonoids, which stabilise the vitamin C and also further colouring. The individual fruits, previously erroneously called seeds, 'Semen Cynosbati', contain fat and ethereal oil, essential oil with vanillin but hardly any vitamin C.
Uses: Fresh rose hips are valued for their vitamins but only insignificant amounts of vitamins must be damaged during the preparation of the pleasant-tasting pulp. Contrary to former belief, the drug has no diuretic effect. It is an ingredient of sudorific teas and serves as a mild laxative.
Side effects: Rose hips have no side effects.
History: Rose hips were used right back in the era of lake dwellings, but were hardly used at all in antiquity.

Dog Rose

PROVINS ROSE
CABBAGE ROSE

Rosa gallica L.
Rosa centifolia L.

Family: Rosaceae.

Description: The Provins rose is a low-growing shrub with far-reaching subterranean stolons. The aerial, whip-like shoots are upright but sometimes branched and about 50 cm (20 in), rarely more than 1 m (3 ft) high. They are thickly furnished with spines and stem glands. The five-lobed, rarely three-lobed leaves are shiny on top, lighter and bluer underneath. The strong protruding lateral veins end in the teeth around the margin of the leaf. The scented flowers are borne mostly singly, rarely twos or threes, on densely-glandular, spiny pedicels. The wide cordate velvety pink to purple petals are about 2–3 cm (½–1 in) long. The globular to pear-shaped calyx develops into a reddish brown false fruit. The cabbage rose, an offspring of the Provins rose, grows taller but does not spread as far. Its flowers are fully double.

Flowering time: Early summer.

Habitat: Provins rose grows well scattered, particularly on chalk, in light deciduous woodland, round the edges of woods and fields and in sunny barren meadows. The cabbage rose has been cultivated in the East since antiquity and many garden varieties have been developed from it.

Distribution: The Provins rose can be found throughout most of Southern and Eastern Europe.

Parts used: Flowers (Flores Rosae).

Harvesting time: Early summer.

Harvesting instructions: Dry petals are gathered before they are fully open. They are dried as quickly as possible in the shade so they are only slightly discoloured. They must be stored dry, the best method being over lime. The drug has a typical rose scent and a harsh, astringent taste.

Ingredients: The roses contain 0.01–0.16 per cent ethereal oil, and large quantities of tannin and flavonoids. The rose oil, oleum rosae, is extracted by distillation on an industrial basis from the flowers of various rose types, but mainly from the R. damascena. Its main ingredients are geraniol, citronellol, nerol and stearoptene. It has a rose fragrance and a harsh taste.

Uses: Due to their tannin content and corresponding astringent effect, rose petals were often used as an infusion for diarrhoea. They were used externally as a gargle and mouthwash. Rose oil is used almost exclusively to improve the taste and smell of medicine. The main user is the cosmetic industry.

Side effects: Rose petals have no known side effects.

History: Roses were used as a drug in Arabian medicine. Bulgaria has been the chief area of their cultivation since the seventeenth century. Previously this was Persia.

Provins Rose Cabbage Rose

BLACKBERRY   *Rubus fruticosus* L.

Family: Rosaceae.
Description: The shoots, known as suckers, usually bear only leaves during the first year then start flowering in their second year. They die after the fruit ripens. The shoots and often the petioles of the leaves are covered in prickles and glands. The leaves are singly or doubly serrated round the edge and covered beneath with white felted tufts of hair. The clustered or paniculate inflorescences spring from the leaf axils and end in a terminal flower that is the first to open. The generally multi-flowered small side branches (partial inflorescences) grow from the axils of the bracts beneath the terminal flower. The five white to reddish petals surround the many upright stamens which are generally longer than the style. The violet-black harvest of fruits consists of the small compound dupes. The type described here is one species that is harvested. Because of the multiplicity of different forms it was subdivided into many subspecies.
Flowering time: Early to mid-summer.
Habitat: The widespread blackberry is often cultivated. It grows wild in light conifer woodlands and deciduous forests, on paths and cutover land.
Distribution: The blackberry is commonly found in Europe and the East.
Parts used: Herbage (Herba Rubi fruticosi); leaves (Folia Rubi fruticosi).
Harvesting time: Late spring to mid-summer.
Harvesting instructions: Only the young branch tips or the leaves should be harvested. The useful material is spread out in a thin layer and dried, being turned frequently. The drug has a weak smell and a harsh taste.
Ingredients: The main constituent of the drug is tannin. Other constituents are organic acids, inosit, vitamin C and flavonoids.
Uses: Because of its astringent characteristics blackberry herbage can be used as a tannin drug for diarrhoea. Normally it is used as a decoction, which is also used externally as a gargle or for skin rashes. If the drug is used solely as a tea it is recommended it should be prepared as an infusion as less tannin is released into the drink and its harsh astringent taste is significantly reduced. The addition of aromatic drugs further improves the taste. In some areas the leaves are also fermented and serve as a substitute for black tea.
Side effects: No side effects are known.
History: Blackberry leaves are among the oldest drugs. Theophrastus, Dioscorides and Galen reported its healing power. Apart from their use for stomach and intestinal complaints, the leaves also served as a sluicing medicine.

Blackberry

RASPBERRY   *Rubus idaeus* L.

Family: Rosaceae.

Description: The raspberry bush produces yellowish brown, pithy shoots 1−2 m (3−6½ ft) high, covered with many scattered blackish-red spines from its branched root. The petiolated leaves are smooth on top but have felted white hair underneath. Their margins are uneven and sharply serrated. The generally nodding flowers are arranged in clustered paniculate inflorescences. The white petals are shorter than the calyx and the numerous stamens, shorter than the style, surround the grey felted ovary. The pleasant-tasting red fruits are each formed of many drupes and are easily separated from the carpophore.

Flowering time: Late spring to early summer and in the mountains up to mid-summer.

Habitat: The raspberry is often found on acid soil, occasionally on chalky soil. It often grows in clearings, hedgerows, thickets and glades, and also in light deciduous and coniferous woodland. It is also cultivated in gardens.

Distribution: The shrub can be found in Sub-Arctic and the cooler temperate zone of the Northern Hemisphere, as well as in East Asia, and North America, where special races are located. In Southern Europe it is restricted to the foothills of the mountains.

Parts used: Herbage (Herba Rubi idaei); leaves (Folia Rubi idaei).

Harvesting time: Late spring to early autumn or fall.

Harvesting instructions: The raspberry shoots or just the leaves are spread out to dry in a thin layer and frequently turned. The drug has a weak smell and a harsh astringent taste.

Ingredients: The raspberry herbage contains tannin with gallic and ellagic acid, flavonoids, organic acids and more vitamin C in the leaves than in the fruit.

Uses: Raspberry herbage belongs to the tannin-containing drugs and is used against diarrhoea because of its astringent effect. A decoction is prepared for this purpose so that much of the tannin goes into the drink. To prepare a tea, an infusion is made so that only minimal amounts of tannin get into the drink and the harsh taste is reduced to a minimum. From the juice of raspberry fruits a syrup (Sirupus Rubi idaei) is prepared by cooking it with sugar. This is used to improve the flavour of bitter tasting medicines.

Side effects: This drug has no known side effects.

History: The Roman Pliny described a medicinal plant called Rubus idaeus. Bock, Fuchs and Valerius Cordus, authors of herbals in the Middle Ages, believed that Pliny was referring to our raspberry bush. The instructions for preparing raspberry syrup are said to originate from Valerius Cordus.

Raspberry

*WILLOW   *Salix* L.

Family: Salicaceae.

Description: Willows are trees or shrubs, occasionally dwarf shrubs. Their alternate leaves have undivided leaf blades with a more or less protruding network of veins. The flowers come in axillary inflorescences or catkins, which usually appear before the leaves. They are normally unisexual and dioecious, i.e. each plant having either male or female flowers. The stamens of the male flowers are often an intense yellow or reddish. The ovary of the female flower develops into a dehiscent capsule which releases many small seeds, each with a tuft of hair. At the base of the stamens or the ovary are two small honey glands which supply the nectar. The male flowers also produce an adhesive pollen. The flowers are particularly sought and pollinated by honey bees.

Flowering time: Early spring to early summer.

Habitat: Willows like damp areas and colonise river meadows and the banks of small streams. Only the dwarf-growing Arctic and Alpine species appear on gravelly hill slopes.

Distribution: Willows are established throughout the Northern Hemisphere, in Europe, Asia and North America. In the north they grow right up to the limits of vegetation being among the most northerly flowering plants. To the south their distribution reaches East India and the Himalayas.

Parts used: Bark (Cortex Salicis).

Harvesting time: Early to mid-spring.

Harvesting instructions: Only the bark of 2- to 3 year-old branches should be taken. It can be quite easily removed by cutting grooves around the branch which are then connected by longitudinal cuts. The bark is pre-dried in the air, then finally dried in artificial heat. The drug is odourless and has a bitter, astringent taste.

Ingredients: The rinds of the various types of willows contain tannin and up to 10 per cent phenolglycoside, amongst them salicin, which is split into saligenin and sugar by the organism. Saligenin is oxidised into salicylic acid. The highest content of the effective ingredients is found in the rind of the purple willow (Salix purpurea).

Uses: Willow bark is described as a vegetable salicylic acid preparation. It was once used in rheumatism and flu decoctions. Since the introduction of synthetic salicylic acid preparations (aspirin) the drug has hardly been used.

Side effects: Salicylic acid preparations are used in relatively high doses. The low content of salicylic in the drug eliminates any risk of poisoning.

History: Willow bark is an old drug which was mentioned by Theophrastus and Dioscorides. Its fever-reducing effect was considered as effective as that of china bark (quinine) so it was used as a "European fever bark" for malaria.

Willow

COMMON SAGE   *Salvia officinalis* L.

Family: Labiatae.
Description: The common sage is a sub-shrub up to 80 cm (32 in) high. The upper part of its stems, which has not become woody, freezes during winter in northern areas. The branches have many sideshoots, later covered with peeling grey-brown bark. The younger shoots are densely felted with spider's-web-like hairs. The opposite, small elliptical leaves have a finely notched margin and finely rugose leaf surfaces which are grey felted when young. The flowers emerge from the axils of bracts in twos to fours and form verticillasters, usually six to eight of them one above the other. The light violet corolla forms a tube at the base about 1 cm long, terminating at the top in a ring of hairs. It is split into a two-part upper lip and three-part lower lip.
Flowering time: Late spring to mid-summer.
Habitat: In its homeland the common sage can be found mainly on chalky slopes. Nowadays it is cultivated on a large scale around Bernburg in West Germany. It is occasionally found naturalised too.
Distribution: As a representative of the warmer regions of Southern Europe common sage can be found from Spain to the northern Balkan countries, Turkey and Northern Syria. It was probably introduced into Italy and the South of France.
Parts used: Leaves (Folia Salviae).
Harvesting time: Late summer to early autumn or fall.
Harvesting instructions: The leaves are gathered in the early afternoon at flowering time, spread out in thin layers and dried as quickly as possible at temperatures up to 40°C. The medicinal drug comes mainly from cultivated plants. It has a camphor-like smell and a harsh, bitter aromatic taste.
Ingredients: Sage leaves contain 1.5−2.5 per cent ethereal oil with approximately 50 per cent thujon and cineol, camphor and borneol; Spanish sage does not contain thujon. Other constituents are tannin, bitter ingredients, saponins and flavonoids, oleanolic and ursolic acids, labiatenic acid.
Uses: This drug was earlier prescribed for night sweats in tuberculosis patients because it suppresses sweat secretions. Due to the combined working of ethereal oil and tannins it has an antiseptic, anti-inflammatory and astringent effect and is used for throat and mouth inflammations. It is also used for inflammatory complaints of the intestinal tract and as an antispasmodic and carminative.
Side effects: Thujon poisoning only occurs when it is misused for abortion purposes.
History: Sage species were valued in the medicine of antiquity and the Middle Ages and in general use.

Common Sage

ELDER

Sambucus nigra L.

Family: Caprifoliaceae.

Description: This species is usually of bushy, but occasionally tree-like growth and can reach a height of 7−10 m (23−33 ft). The bark of the main stem and older branches is grey-brown and fissured, that on the younger branches green with many grey spots called bark pores or lenticels. The branches contain a soft, white pith and the opposite leaves are imparipinnate. The flowers have a strong sweet scent and stand in umbel-like inflorescences (cymes) at the ends of the branches. Each cyme has five main branches. The five white to yellowish, joined petals enclose five stamens and the tripartite ovary, which develops into a juicy blue-black three-seeded berry.

Flowering time: Late spring to mid-summer.

Habitat: The elder can be found in original locations like damp areas in open woods, stony, bushy places and by riversides, in gulleys, hollows and sometimes in gardens.

Distribution: The elder appears nearly all over Europe. Its northern limit runs through Southern Sweden and Lithuania. It is distributed from the Danube estuary via Turkey and the Caucasus to Western Siberia.

Parts used: Flowers (Flores Sambuci).

Harvesting time: Early to mid-summer.

Harvesting instructions: As flowering begins the flowers were gathered in dry weather and dried immediately at temperatures up to 40°C in a well ventilated place. When dried the drug should be stored in airtight containers. It has a characteristic smell, tastes sweet and slimy, but later becomes rough.

Ingredients: The elder flower contains flavonoids, little ethereal oil, some tannin, mucilage compounds, rutin and the hydrogen-cyanide glycoside sambunigrin.

Uses: Elder flower tea drunk as hot as possible in large quantities is a sudorific and used particularly for colds and feverish illnesses. The hot water, made palatable by the ethereal oil and the effect of the flavonoid glycosides, is particularly effective but only the required quantities should be drunk.

Side effects: Fresh elder flowers cause skin irritation.

History: The elder was already in use during the era of lake dwellings. Hippocrates used the fruit particularly, and Theophrastus, Dioscorides and Pliny mention the plant which was greatly treasured during the Middle Ages.

Elder

SOAPWORT

Saponaria officinalis L.

Family: Caryophyllaceae.

Description: This 30−70 cm (12−28 in) high plant overwinters by means of its roots which can become as thick as one's finger, from which fertile and infertile shoots emerge in spring, creeping like stolons. The round stems are segmented, slightly thicker at the nodes and usually branched towards the top. The opposite leaves are arranged crosswise at the nodes and the slightly fragrant flowers form dense clusters at the ends of the stems and in the axils of the leaves. The flowers have swollen pale green calyces and the pink to white petals are unguiculate. The ovary has two thread-like, outward-bent styles and develops into a single-celled capsule.

Flowering time: Early summer to early autumn or fall.

Habitat: Soapwort is found particularly on river-meadows from the lowlands up into the alpine foothills but also near fences, walls, roadsides and round fields.

Distribution: The plant grows in Central and Southern Europe, westwards to England and northwards to Scandinavia, eastwards across Turkey and Central Asia to Japan and in the north-east to Siberia. In North America it is only an introduced plant.

Parts used: Root (Radix Saponariae).

Harvesting time: Late summer to early autumn or fall.

Harvesting instructions: Generally the roots of biennial plants are collected. The useful material must be dried at temperatures up to 60°C. This way the ingredients remain effective. The drug has a weak smell and tastes sweet at first, but later rough and lingering.

Ingredients: The root of the soapwort contains a mixture of saponins as effective ingredients.

Uses: The saponaria saponines are poisonous, and large doses can cause vomiting. They were formerly described as sapotoxins. When taken in therapeutic doses they increase the secretions of the glands in the bronchial tract and so are used as an expectorant for complaints of the lungs. Soapwort was used industrially as a detergent. It was added to stain removers and other cleansing materials because of its foaming effect.

Side effects: Contains saponines which can cause local irritation.

History: In antiquity the saponine drugs were collected together under the name of struthion. Soapwort was used as a medicine in the Middle Ages. Like the various kinds of primrose, this drug was used as a substitute for the saponine-containing exotic drug, senega root, after the World War 1.

Soapwort

BROOM   *Sarothamnus scoparius* (L.) KOCH

Family: Papilionaceae.

Description: The common broom is a shrub up to 2 m (6½ ft) high, rarely a small 3−5 m (10−17 ft)high tree with a very strong, woody taproot with lateral roots which have root nodules, like many papilionaceous plants. Many green twiggy branched shoots spread from the short main stem, but die back to the main branches during severe winters. The five-sided green twigs have alternate tripartite leaves which soon drop off. Only the long upper shoots carry simple petioled leaves. The flowers stand singly or in pairs on contracted short shoots and appear to form a clustering inflorescence. The brilliant yellow corolla consists of the vertical standard petal, the two wings and the keel. When ripe the longish seed pod catapults the many seeds far afield with a crackling noise.

Flowering time: Late spring to early summer.

Habitat: The common broom prefers sandy, dry, chalk-free soil. It is found particularly on heathland in Central Europe, a part of the Atlantic climatic region.

Distribution: Its original home is considered to be Central and Western Europe. In the north, its limit runs across Southern Scotland to Southern Scandinavia, but its eastern limit is not certain.

Parts used: Herbage (Herba Sarothamni scoparii).

Harvesting time: Late winter and mid-autumn or fall.

Harvesting instructions: The herbage, particularly that of the alkaloid-rich upper branchtips, was cut off and carefully dried. The drug has a spicy smell and an aromatic, bitter taste.

Ingredients: The herbage of the common broom contains up to 3 per cent alkaloids with spartein as the main alkaloid. Furthermore it contains the drug flavonoid glycoside.

Uses: The drug is valued only as a raw material for the pharmaceutical industry. Spartein is used medicinally for heart and circulatory problems during heart rhythm disorders. In obstetrics it is used to induce and intensify labour.

Side effects: Poisoning by the plant or spartein is rare. It resembles mild nicotine poisoning.

History: In his "Pharmacology" Dioscorides refers to a medicinal plant by the name of "Spartion". Galen called it "Sparte". It is possible that these referred to the common broom, which Linnaeus called Spartium scoparium.

Broom

SUMMER SAVORY   *Satureja hortensis* L.

Family: Labiatae.

Description: This annual plant which seldom survives the winter has a single stem up to 30 cm(1 ft) high and bears more or less bushy branches at the nodes. The branches are almost equal in height and coloured green or reddish. The downy-haired shoots have numerous gland scales which account for its aromatic smell. The leaves have sunken glands which show up as light spots when seen against the light. The corolla is lilac to whitish and only slightly taller than the teeth of the calyx. It is extended into a tube at the front with a short upper lip and slightly longer three-lobed lower lip. The bell-shaped green or violet calyx is covered in downy hair. Smooth nuts, grey-green to dark brown and 1 to 1.5 mm long, develop from the ovary.

Flowering time: Mid-summer to early autumn or fall.

Habitat: Summer savory is cultivated in almost every herb garden as a culinary herb and has become naturalised to some extent.

Distribution: Summer savory probably originated around the Black Sea and the Eastern Mediterranean from Iran to Yugoslavia, Northern and Central Italy as far as the Maritime Alps. In the Caucasus it grows up to 1600 m (4570 ft) and in the Alps up to 1500 m (4900 ft).

Parts used: Herbage (Herba Saturejae).

Harvesting time: Mid to late summer.

Harvesting instructions: Either the whole herbage or the upper tips of the plant are cut off with shears and dried by tying the material in bundles and hanging them up, or spreading it in a thin layer. The dried drug must be stored in an airtight container. It has a pleasant, spicy smell and a sharp burning taste.

Ingredients: The savory summer contains approximately 0.1 to 2 per cent ethereal oil with approximately 30 per cent carvacrol, 20 per cent cymol, cymen, caryophylls, cardins and others. Furthermore it contains tannin, mucilage and resin.

Uses: The drug was mainly used for diarrhoea. Apart from its ethereal oil and particularly its carvocrol content, the tannin is also effective. It is said to have a thirst-quenching effect on diabetics. It is used as a culinary herb in the home and in sausage-making factories.

Side effects: Using the drug can lead to skin rashes.

History: Summer savory was probably known in antiquity as a culinary herb. It is mentioned in Charlemagne's "Capitulare". The botanists of the Middle Ages wrote about the plant. The ethereal oil was mentioned for the first time in 1582.

Summer Savory

WHITE MUSTARD

Sinapis alba L.

Family: Cruciferae.

Description: White mustard is an annual plant. The thin yellow-ish-white, branched root produces an upright, grooved stem, about 30 to 60 cm (1−2 ft) high. The leaves are lyrate-pinnatifid to pinnatisect. The flowers form an umbel-like inflorescence when in bloom, which later extends as the axis stretches and becomes looser. The inflorescences are borne at the ends of the main stem and the branches. In full bloom the four obtuse sepals are held horizontally. Each of the light yellow petals is narrowed at the base to form a claw. At the base of the stamens there are three green honey glands which makes them particularly popular with honey bees. The 2−4 cm (½−1½ in) long fruit is a pod densely covered in bristly hairs. The stout (false) septum is divided into two cells, each containing two or three globular, brown to whitish seeds.

Flowering time: Early to mid-summer, depending when they are sown.

Habitat: The plant is cultivated particularly in warm areas, but only occasionally in mountainous places. It is also found growing naturalised.

Distribution: White mustard probably originated in the Mediterranean area but this is not known for certain.

Parts used: Seeds (Semen Erucae).

Harvesting time: Mid to late summer.

Harvesting instructions: The mustard seeds are easily attacked by mildew, so they must be dried in a well ventilated place. The drug is odourless and tastes mild and oily at first, later sharp and burning.

Ingredients: The seeds of the white mustard pepper contain 2.5 per cent of the glycoside sinalbin, which, in the presence of water, splits into the non-volatile sinalbinsen oil by enzyme myrosinase.

Uses: The main effective constituent of the drug is sinalbin mustard oil. Drug extracts inhibit the growth of bacteria. White mustard seeds can be used as a skin irritant for rheumatic and neuralgic pain. It has a milder effect than black mustard (Brassica nigra) and is more suitable when used internally for chronic indigestion. Table mustard produced from Semen Erucae retains its sharp taste since the mustard oil is not volatile.

Side effects: Used in therapeutic doses the drug has no side effects.

History: Pliny refers to three species of mustard. It is assumed that white mustard, a native of the Mediterranean area, was among them. In the past it was often preferred to black mustard.

White Mustard

†BITTERSWEET   *Solanum dulcamara* L.

Family: Solanaceae.

Description: The lower part of the bittersweet is a woody sub-shrub, whose upper branches die off in autumn. The prostrated or climbing branches, about 2 m (6½ ft) (seldom up to 5 m (17 ft)) long, are clothed with alternate leaves. The many-flowered, paniculate inflorescences droop. The dark violet, occasionally white or pink, petals, like the violet sepals, are joined together at the base. Its pointed, initially horizontal projecting, free tips are later bent back and have two green, white bordered spots at the base. The brilliant golden-yellow colour of the tubular anthers, joined together to form a tube, makes the flower clearly visible. The fruit is an oval scarlet-red pendulous berry with many seeds.

Flowering time: Summer.

Habitat: The plant is particularly found in damp scrub, on stream and riverbanks and meadow woodlands.

Distribution: Bittersweet is a native of Europe, as well as North Africa and Western Asia to India, Japan and China.

Parts used: Young branches (Stipites Dulcamarae).

Harvesting time: Mid-autumn or fall.

Harvesting instructions: The 2−3 year old shoots of the plant are collected in autumn when the leaves have fallen and are then cut up and dried. The drug is nearly odourless and tastes bitter, but later becomes sweet.

Beware! Bittersweet is a poisonous plant, the berries being the most poisonous part.

Ingredients: The drug contains glyco-alkaloid and steroid saponins. Other ingredients are tannin and pectin, solasodine, soladulcidine.

Uses: The branches of the bittersweet were formerly used for all chronic skin complaints which were accompanied by itching, and for chronic bronchitis and asthma. The drug is only used nowadays for homeopathy and sometimes in folk medicine as a "blood cleanser", as a diuretic and against rheumatism, gout and also skin complaints. Presumably the saponine type ingredients are the effective agents.

Poisonous effect: Poisoning occurs mainly among children who eat tempting berries. It leads to excitement of the central nervous system, tongue paralysis, vomiting and dizziness.

History: The medicinal use of bittersweet was first reported in the middle of the sixteenth century. Due to its taste the drug was once called Dulcisamara.

Bittersweet

POTATO   *Solanum tuberosum* L.

Family: Solanaceae.
Description: The potato is a 50 cm (20 in), occasionally up to 1 m (3 ft) high, herbaceous perennial. Apart from its long fibrous roots it produces many underground stolons at whose ends the potato tubers form. The alternate-leaved stems are green to red-brown with adpressed hairs. The flowers are borne in cluster-like inflorescences at the ends of the stems. The calyx is five-lobed, and the white, reddish or blue corona consists of five petals fused together. The brilliant yellow anthers lean towards each other to form a cone shape. The ovate, two-celled ovary develops into a fleshy, green berry the size of a cherry, containing many seeds.
Flowering time: Summer.
Distribution and habitat: The original species from which our potato has been developed are to be found in the Andes from Peru, Bolivia and Chile where the natives used wild potatoes as well as cultivating them. The history of the introduction of the potato into Europe is shrouded in darkness. About 1560 the first potatoes reached Spain, but it was only in the eighteenth century that the potato became widespread. Nowadays potatoes even grow in the Alps up to the 2000 m (6500 ft) contour. In the North it is cultivated in Greenland and Iceland right up to the permanent ice limit.
Medicinal use: It is the starch, Amylum Solani, extracted from the potato tuber and obtained by elutriation, washing, settling and decanting that is used medicinally. The starch is extracted on an industrial scale. After careful cleaning the potatoes are ground down and the mush is washed several times, then the starch is allowed to settle. It is again repeatedly washed, dried at a temperature up to 40°C and finally rolled. To prevent the starch being turned brown by oxidising polyphenols, sulphur dioxide is added to the rinse water. Potato starch is a white powder which makes a crunching sound when ground down. It is odourless and tasteless.
Uses: Potato starch is used pharmaceutically as a basis for dusting powder and toilet powder. Various substances can be added to it. It has a cooling and anti-flammatory effect and because it swells the starch is used as a distributory compound in the manufacture of tablets, for diluting powders and to adjust the concentration of fixed amounts of substances which must be used at a certain percentage.
Side effects: The unripe fruits (potato berries) contain about 1 per cent, the potato shoots about 0.5 per cent and the tubers a maximum of 0.06 per cent highly poisonous solanin, which is dissolved in the water when the tubers are boiled.

Potato

GOLDEN ROD

Solidago virgaurea L.

Family: Compositae.

Description: This herbaceous plant, growing about 1 m (3 ft) high, overwinters by means of its cylindrical, nodular rootstock. In the upper part of the simple, upright stems there are loosely arranged leaves. The many flowers are about 7—18 mm long. The cylindrical calyculus consisists of many imbricately superimposed bare scales. There are about 8—12 female ray florets on each yellow flower. The styles and stigmas project from the hermaphrodite five-toothed disc florets, the anthers, stuck together to form tubes, from the corona. The hairy fruits are about 4 mm long.

Flowering time: Mid-summer to early autumn or fall.

Habitat: Golden rod thrives on both chalky and acid soils and can be found from the dune woods of the Baltic to the stunted woods on the mountains. It is often found in light dry woods, undergrowth, on slopes and road embankments, as well as on rocks and walls.

Distribution: The plant can be found all over Europe and Northern and Western Asia except for the far north. It grows to North Africa in the south and is also at home in North America.

Parts used: Herbage (Herba Virgaureae).

Harvesting time: Mid-summer to early autumn or fall.

Harvesting instructions: The aerial parts of the plant are cut off with shears while in flower and carefully dried in a thin layer. Plants whose flowers are wilting should not be collected. The drug is odourless and has a weak astringent taste.

Ingredients: The herbage of the golden rod contains saponin, flavonoids, tannin, bitter constituents and ethereal oil.

Uses: Its saponine and flavanoid content give the drug a strong diuretic effect, so it is an ingredient of many bladder and kidney decoctions. It was once used for gout and rheumatism. It was used externally in folk medicine for ulcers and wounds that were difficult to heal.

Side effects: No side effects have been observed when using this drug. However, it is said to have led to the poisoning of cattle.

History: There are no reliable records of the use of this drug in antiquity, but it is not impossible that golden rod was used as a medicine at that time. It was one of the valued medicines of the Middle Ages. Hieronymus Bock mentions it in his herbals.

Golden Rod

COMFREY   *Symphytum officinale* L.

Family: Boraginaceae.

Description: The plant is a herbaceous perennial 60 cm (2 ft) high with a short, stout root from which spread a number of strong, mucilaginous roots, about 30 cm (1 ft) long which are black outside and white inside. The upright, fleshy stems are branched only towards the top, and appear angular as the leaves extend down the stem with their 2−3 mm wide wings. The stems and the nerves which protrude underneath the leaves are covered in stiff bristly hairs. The upper surface of the rugose reticulately veined leaves is also hairy. The pedicellated, five-lobed flowers arise from a many-flowered, double circinus (rolled up formation) in the axils of the upper leaves. The red-violet or yellowish-white corolla forms a bell-shaped tube which broadens at the front and is covered with velvety hair outside. The dark violet anthers on the stamens are longer than the filaments.

Flowering time: Late spring to mid-summer.

Habitat: The plant lives in damp places and grows in wet meadows beside streams and on the banks of rivers and ponds.

Distribution: Comfrey can be found over most of Europe, in the north to Ireland, Scotland, Central Scandinavia, Southern Finland, and Karelia, in the east to Western Siberia and Turkey, via the northern Balkan countries, Central Italy to Central Spain.

Parts used: Root (Radix Consolidae).

Harvesting time: Early to mid-spring and early to mid-autumn or fall.

Harvesting instructions: The roots are dug out, freed from earth, washed, and laid out or threaded on strings to dry. Larger parts are split longitudinally. The drug is odourless and has an aromatic, slightly sweet taste which changes to a sharp, bitter, astringent after-taste.

Ingredients: Main ingredients of the comfrey root are 0.6−0.8 per cent allantoin and mucilage; furthermore it contains amongst others tannin and biogene amine such as asparagin and choline, and is rich in silica.

Uses: The drug is an old folk medicine used externally for slow-healing wounds, broken bones and periostitis. Allantoin is the effective ingredient. The root is also used for straining, bruising, tenosynovitis, effusions of blood, thrombosis and other conditions. It is sometimes used internally for gastritis and stomach ulcers by reason of its mucilage content.

Side effects: The root is free of alkaloids and without side effects.

History: Galen referred to the plant by different names. It was also used medicinally during the Middle Ages, mainly externally. The pulp prepared from fresh plants was applied to broken bones.

Comfrey

TANSY   *Tanacetum vulgare* L.

Family: Compositae.

Description: Tansy is a tuft-forming perennial plant which grows up to 1½ m (5 ft) high. Its thick, branched, partly woody root has many heads. From this arise several stiffly erect, angular, partly brown-red shaded, slightly hairy stems. The alternate leaves up to 25 cm (10 in) long are simply or doubly laciniated and have fine glandular spotting. Many hemispherical flowers, flattened on top, are arranged close together in cyme formation. All the flowers are tubular and the golden yellow hermaphrodite disc florets each have a five-toothed crown. The ray florets which are female and three-toothed on top, can be missing at times. The five-ribbed fruits each have a small, toothed crown. The whole plant, but particularly its flowers, has a strange aromatic smell and tastes unpleasantly bitter.

Flowering time: Mid-summer to early autumn or fall.

Habitat: This widely distributed plant grows mainly in groups beside footpaths and the outskirts of woods, on banks, ditches, riverbanks and railway embankments.

Distribution: Tansy is found across large parts of the Northern Hemisphere, such as Europe, North Asia and North America.

Parts used: Herbage (Herba Tanaceti); flowers (Flores Tanaceti).

Harvesting time: Herbage, mid-summer to mid-autumn or fall; flowers, mid-summer to early autumn or fall.

Harvesting instructions: The uppermost part of the herbage is cut off with shears while in bloom during dry weather in 20–30 cm (8–12 in) lengths, then bundled and hung in a well ventilated shady place to dry.

After the umbels have been gathered during dry weather the individual flowers are cut off and quickly dried in the shade. The drug smells aromatic like camphor and has a repulsive bitter, herby taste.

Ingredients: The herbage of the tansy contains 0.2–0.6 per cent, ethereal oil and the flowers up to 1.5 per cent. The main ingredients are thujon and the bitter constituent, tanacetin.

Uses: The drug was previously used as a vermifuge by reason of its thujon content but has been replaced by less dangerous and more effective drugs.

Side effects: Poisoning by this plant is very rare, but misuse of the ethereal oil for abortion purposes can cause vomiting, unconsciousness, cramp and damage to the kidney and liver with fatal consequences, or death by asphyxiation.

History: Tansy has been used as a medicine since the eighteenth century, and the oil as a vermifuge since the sixteenth century.

Tansy

DANDELION

Taraxacum officinale
WIGGERS

Family: Compositae.

Description: The dandelion survives from year to year by means of its long taproot, blackish brown on the ouside, which is covered at the top with a little woolly hair. It becomes as thick as one's finger, is white inside and like the whole plant contains milky sap. The often multi-headed taproot forms a generous leaf rosette. The single or many single-headed flower stems are hollow and completely bare. The calyx consists of many involucres of which the inner ones stand erect and envelop the flower. The receptacle later becomes almost globular because all the leaflets of the calyculus bend backwards. The heads bear many gold and pale yellow flowers. The light to black fruitlets have a broad white, ray-like pappus which the wind blows far and wide. The species was divided into many sub-species.

Flowering time: Mid-spring to early autumn or fall.

Habitat: This plant grows on all types of soil from the plains to the mountains, in meadows, fields, pastures and in light woods.

Distribution: This plant can be found in most parts of the Northern Hemisphere.

Parts used: Whole plant with root (Radix Taraxaci cum herba).

Harvesting time: Mid to late spring.

Harvesting instructions: The plant is dug out before it flowers, freed from earth and dried in artificial heat up to 40°C. The drug has a slight odour and a weak bitter taste.

Ingredients: The main ingredients of the dandelion are bitter constituents, such as taraxacin, and flavonoids. The milky sap contains cerylalcohol, lactucerol, taraxacin, inosit and cholin, the root inulin, tannin and some ethereal oil, the leaves contain vitamin C and the flowers xanthophylle.

Uses: When harvested in spring, the plant has a slight inulin content and is used as a bitter constituent for loss of appetite and stomach upsets. The drug promotes the secretion of gall and is an ingredient of liver and gall-bladder decoctions.

Side effects: When children suck the milky sap from the stem of the plant it can result in taraxacin poisoning, with sickness, vomiting, diarrhoea and serious heart rhythm disorders.

History: The Arab doctors Rhazes and Ibn Sina (Avicenna) first mentioned the dandelion but it is assumed that the knowledge of its medicinal value was taken from the Greeks. The sixteenth century herbals also recommend the drug.

Dandelion

†ARBOR VITAE

Thuja occidentalis L.

Family: Cupressaceae.

Description: This evergreen tree growing up to 20 m (66 ft)has a pyramidal crown and horizontal branches. The stout trunk can reach a diameter of up to 1¼ m (4 ft). Its bark is reddish brown and usually split into narrow strips. The freely branching shoots are flat, and the twiglets pressed together are dark green on top and pale green underneath. The male flowers are globular, while the females are oval cones up to 8 mm long, at first green and upright, but later nodding and light brown. They ripen in their first year. The cone's scales are arranged in an imbricate fashion in four or five pairs. The second and third pair are larger and fertile. Two narrow seeds pressed together appear under each scale and are surrounded by a small wing.

The Western Arbor Vitae differs from the Eastern Arbor Vitae (T. orientalis) by its horizontally spread out twiglets which are vertical in the latter. Many similar types are distinguished.

Flowering time: Mid to late spring.

Habitat: In its homeland the arbor vitae grows in chalky, marshy areas. In Germany it is generously planted in gardens and cemetries.

Distribution: The tree's home is Eastern North America. It was introduced into Europe about 1550.

Parts used: Tips of twigs (Summitates Thujae).

Harvesting time: Late spring to early autumn or fall.

Harvesting instructions: Small, young twig tips are cut off with shears and spread out to dry in a shady well ventilated place. The drug has a strong aromatic smell and sharp, camphor-like taste. Beware! This plant is poisonous!

Ingredients: Summitates Thujae contains up to 1 per cent ethereal oil, the flavonoid glycoside quercitrin (formerly called Thujin), tannin and resin. The ethereal oil is extracted from the branch tips by water distillation, the main constituent being thujon; apart from which it contains pines, camphor, borneol and fenchon. It smells like camphor and tastes bitter.

Uses: Because it is poisonous, the drug is no longer used. It was earlier used in folk medicine as a linament for rheumatism and gout. It was misused for abortion purposes, but was not always effective even in fatal doses.

Toxic effect: The toxicity of the drug is due to its thujon content which causes strong locally irritating sensations, cramp, bleeding of the stomach and intestinal mucous membrane and the heart muscle and has fatal consequences through the destruction of the kidneys and liver.

History: The oil's vermifuge effect was discovered in 1828.

Arbor Vitae

WILD THYME

Thymus serpyllum L.

Family: Labiatae.

Description: Wild thyme is a dwarf shrub about 10−15 cm (4−6 in) high with slightly woody branches, and usually dense mat-forming growth, due to its habit of forming stolons. The ascending or prostrate stems are cylindrical or square. The leaves vary greatly in shape. The individual flowers in the terminal inflorescences appear several together in verticillasters in the axils of the leaves. The calyx tube is five-toothed and its throat is covered with a ring of long white hairs. The light to dark purple-red 3−6 mm long corolla has only a short tube. The style has a two-part stigma. Wild thyme differs from garden thyme (T. vulgaris L) mainly by its creeping, very strongly rooted stolons. The garden thyme's ascending or upright branches never root.

Flowering time: Late spring to early autumn or fall.

Habitat: Wild thyme can be found in dry, sunny areas, on both acid and strongly alkaline soils.

Distribution: This plant can be found in the whole of temperate Eurasia from the Mediterranean and Western India northwards to Greenland, Iceland, Northern Siberia and Kamchatka. The wild thyme was introduced into North America by settlers.

Parts used: Flowering herbage (Herba Serpylli).

Harvesting time: Summer.

Harvesting instructions: The flower shoots were cut off with shears and spread out in a thin layer to dry. The drug has a pleasant, spicy, aromatic smell and a strong, spicy, harsh bitter taste.

Ingredients: the herbage of wild thyme contains 0.2−0.6 per cent ethereal oil, whose main constituents are cymol, apart from carvacrol and thymol while other species contain citral and pines. The drug also contains tannin, bitter constituents (serpyllin) and flavonoids.

Uses: Wild thyme herbage was used for coughs, though less frequently than that of garden thyme. Because of its bitter constituents it was used as a stomachic and was added to baths because of its aromatic fragrance.

Side effects: No sid effects have occurred when using this drug and none are to be expected.

History: Wild thyme is an old medicinal plant, but it is not known if it was used in antiquity. It was used as a healing plant in the Middle Ages, particularly for female complaints. It also played a role in Central and Eastern Europe as a lucky plant, while it had a bad reputation among superstitious people in England and France.

Wild Thyme

GARDEN THYME   *Thymus vulgaris* L.

Family: Labiatae.

Description: This woody sub-shrub, generally an annual in Central and Northern Europe, reaches a height of 30 cm (1 ft). Its strong taproot is finely branched towards the bottom. Its erect or ascending stems are thickly branched towards the top. The square-stemmed branches are covered on top with short hair and the opposite leaves, whose margins are involuted, are covered with short grey felt, particularly beneath. The spike-like inflorescence consists of verticillasters in the axils of the leaves. The bilabiate calyx is closed by hair until it fruits. The pink to lilac corolla comprises an undivided upper lip and a three-lobed lower lip.

Flowering time: Late spring to mid-autumn or fall.

Habitat: Large areas of garden thyme are cultivated in Central Europe as a culinary herb, and it has become naturalised to some extent in warmer surroundings.

Distribution: Garden thyme is generally distributed through the North-Western Mediterranean area and is also cultivated in the rest of Europe to about latitude 70°.

Parts used: Flowering herbage (Folia Thymi).

Harvesting time: Early to mid-summer and early autumn or fall.

Harvesting instructions: The stripped leaves and flowers were spread out in a thin layer in a well ventilated room to dry. The drug has a strong aromatic smell and taste.

Ingredients: The thymian herbage contains ethereal oil, approximately 10 per cent tannin, bitter constituents, saponins and flavonoids. The content of ethereal oil is at its highest in the early hours of the afternoon and is also dependent on location; German thymian contains 0.4−3.4 per cent, French plants contain 1.75−5.4 per cent ethereal oil. The main constituents of Oleum Thymi are thymol or its isomeres carvacrol and cymol, borneol, bornylacetat, cineol, linalool and pines. It smells and tastes very spicy.

Uses: Thyme has an anti-spasmodic and expectorant effect and because of its thymol is a discharging agent prescribed for coughs, particularly whooping cough and bronchitis. The drug has an anti-spasmodic effect during flatulence. It is used for diarrhoea by reason of its tannin content and astringent effect and its bitter constituents stimulate the appetite. Because of its phenols, thymol or carvacrol, thyme oil acts as a disinfectant, so it is added to gargles, mouthwashes and toothpastes.

Side effects: Poisoning by this plant is unknown. Using preparations containing thymol for a long time is said to cause hyperactivity of the thyroid glands. Thymol colours urine green to black and must not be prescribed for frail people since they are very sensitive to pure substances.

History: Various species of thyme were used in antiquity as spices and medicines. The drug has been used in Central Europe since the sixteenth century.

Garden Thyme

SMALL-LEAVED LIME   *Tilia cordata* MILL.

Family: Tiliaceae.

Description: The small-leaved lime is a tree over 25 m (182 ft) high with a strong, branched taproot and far-reaching lateral roots. It has a wide, globular crown. The young shoots are covered in fine hair to start with. The asymmetric leaves, slightly cordate at the base, are almost smooth. The paniculate inflorescence has three to 16 flowers, and its stem is partly fused with the greenish yellow, tongue-shaped bract wing. The flowers consist of five small sepals, five yellowish-white petals almost double the length, and up to 30 stamens and the ovary. The seeds in the single-seeded globular fruits are smaller than those of the large-leaved lime (T. platyphyllos SCOP.) which differs from the small-leaved lime mainly by its hairy leaves and its two to eight-flowered inflorescence. The flowers give out a strong sweet smell.

Flowering time: Early to mid-summer.

Habitat: Limes generally grow scattered in mixed deciduous and coniferous woodland, rarely in colonies of the one species, from the lowlands into the wooded foothills of the mountains. The small-leaved lime is usually a tree of the lowlands and protected mountain ranges while the large-leaved lime makes less demands. This popular tree is often planted in streets and on farms.

Distribution: Both species of lime are limited in their natural distribution to Europe. The large-leaved lime does not appear as far north as the small-leaved lime.

Parts used: Inflorescences (Flores Tiliae).

Harvesting time: Early to mid-summer.

Harvesting instructions: The inflorescences together with their bracts were picked on a sunny day around midday. The harvest was spread out in a thin layer in the shade and occasionally turned. The drug has a pleasant aromatic smell, lost when it is dried and an aromatic, slimy taste.

Ingredients: The flowers of the small-leaved lime and the large-leaved lime contain mucilage, tannin, approximately 0.04 per cent ethereal oil with farnesol, geraniol, eugenol and others which create the fragrance. They also contain flavonoids.

Uses: The drug was prescribed as a sudorific for colds. As with elderflowers the ingredients of the lime flowers have no proven sudorific effect, but their flavour and mucilage content makes it possible to take enough hot water to promote sweating. The ethereal oil is used in the cosmetics industry.

Side effects: The drug has no side effects.

History: Lime flowers were not used in antiquity and not mentioned by the great botanists of the Middle Ages. But lime charcoal was used medicinally as an absorbent for diarrhoea, poisoning and intestinal sepsis before animal charcoal was introduced in the fifteenth century.

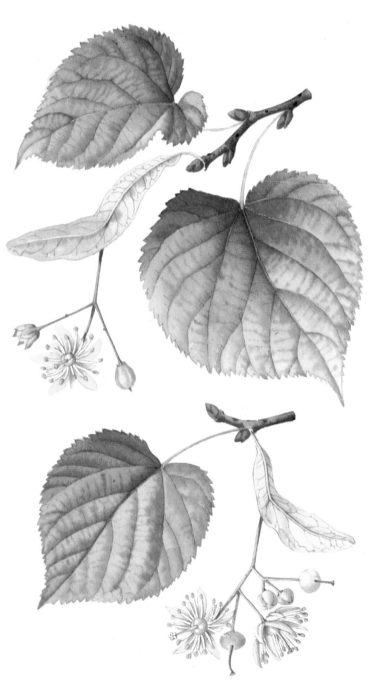

Small-leaved Lime

COLTSFOOT   *Tussilago farfara* L.

Family: Compositae.
Description: Coltsfoot survives the winter by means of its underground rootstock which is covered in scale leaves. Early in spring the flower stems develop, each bearing a single flower head, and reach 30 cm (1 ft) long by fruiting time. They are covered in green to reddish scale leaves and hairs right up to the golden-yellow capitulums. A bell-shaped calyx shrouds the flowers, which consist of many female ray florets with 30 to 40 disc florets in the centre. Each of the many fruits has a pappus. The basal leaves form only after flowering, and are felted with white wool on both sides at first but soon become bare on top. The similar but much larger leaves of winter heliotrope (petasites species) are less hairy except when young, furthermore the coltsfoot's petioles are compressed at the sides and smooth (not ribbed).
Flowering time: Late winter to mid-spring.
Habitat: As one of the first spring flowerers, the coltsfoot enlivens pathsides, fields, gravelly slopes and railway embankments with its brilliant yellow flowers. It prefers damp, marly soil.
Distribution: The genus, consisting of just the one species, can be found in Europe, Western and Northern Asia and the mountains of North Africa.
Parts used: Leaves (Folia Fararae); flowers (Flores Farfarae).
Harvesting time: Leaves, late spring to early summer; flowers, early to mid-spring.
Harvesting instructions: When harvesting the leaves, care must be taken not to confuse them with those of the winter heliotrope which is known in the vernacular as the "large coltsfoot". The leaves should be spread out individually and dried in warm air up to 40°C during which they should not be allowed to roll up as they easily rot. They should not be turned. The drug is nearly odourless and has a slimy harsh bitter taste.
The flower heads are collected without their pedicels before they are fully open and dried in a thin layer. The drug has a honey-like aroma and tastes slimy, harsh and bitter.
Ingredients: The leaves contain mucilage, flavonoids, tannin, inulin, some ethereal oil and bitter constituents; the flowers contain mucilage, flavonoids, traces of tannin, phytosterols, arnidiol, and faradiol.
Uses: Coltsfoot leaves and flowers were prescribed as an enveloping agent and expectorant. They are constituents of various cough mixtures and are used for all respiratory illnesses, coughs and hoarseness.
Side effects: The drug has no side effects.
History: The medicinal value of coltsfoot, and particularly its leaves, was well known in antiquity. Pliny, Dioscorides and Galen mentioned it. The plant was also used for healing purposes in the Middle Ages.

Coltsfoot

STINGING NETTLE

Urtica dioica L.

Family: Urticaceae.

Description: The stinging nettle is a 30−150 cm (1−5 ft) high herbaceous plant that survives from year to year by means of its wide branching underground rootstock. In spring it produces erect unbranched square shoots covered in short bristles and long leaves with stinging hairs on both sides. The flowers are borne in inflorescences in the leaf axils towards the tops of the shoots. Each plant forms either male or female flowers which are pollinated by the wind. The male flowers project stiffly, while the females hang down, forming longer sideshoots. The small, green individual flowers with four petals are insignificant, the males have four stamens. The slightly smaller small nettle (U. urens L.) is similar to the stinging nettle, but male and female flowers appear together in one inflorescence. It also has no rootstock, being an annual.

Flowering time: Early summer to mid-autumn or fall.

Habitat: The stinging nettle occurs in the main close to human settlements, but also grows in meadow copses and on river banks.

Distribution: The stinging nettle is cosmopolitan, being distributed all over the globe and missing only from Tropical and Southern Africa and the Polar regions.

Parts used: Herbage (Herba Urticae).

Harvesting time: Summer.

Harvesting instructions: Stinging nettle and small nettle plants up to 20 cm (8 in) high are cut off with shears while in flower and dried. The drug is odourless and tastes slightly bitter.

Ingredients: The stinging hair of the drug contains acetylcholin, histamine, serotonin and formic, acetic and butyric acid. The herbage contains a large quantity of chlorophyll (up to 1 per cent), xanthophyll, carotinoid, silicic acid, glucokinine and vitamin C.

Uses: Nettle herbage has a small diuretic effect and is still included in gall-bladder and kidney, gout and rheumatism decoctions. An extract is added to hair lotions and helps with the extraction of chlorophyll.

Side effects: Externally the ingredients of the stinging hairs form painful itchy swellings. Using material from older nettle plants can cause stomach irritation, burning skin over the whole body and kidney damage.

History: The Greeks already knew the medicinal value of the stinging nettle in antiquity. The herbals of the Middle Ages also gave extensive details about its healing effects. Due to its stinging effect the plant has played a considerable role in superstition.

Stinging Nettle

BILBERRY   *Vaccinium myrtillus* L.

Family: Ericaceae.
Description: The bilberry is a small heavily branched shrub up to
50 cm (20 in)high with wide-spreading subterranean stolons. The
plant can reach an age of 30 years. The green, sharp edged
branches bear finely serrated green leaves in summer. The greenish to reddish, pedicellated flowers are arranged singly in the leaf
axils. The green calyx is united with the ovary and the petals are
globular and urn-shaped with a small opening. The epigynous
ovary develops into the familiar blue-black, many-seeded bilberry, which is usually covered in bloom.
Flowering time: Mid-spring to late summer.
Habitat: The bilberry is an inhabitant of acid soils and grows in
sufficiently damp woods on naturally rocky soil or sand, where it
usually covers wide areas. It forms an important part of dwarf
shrub heathland and scrub on the higher mountains and moorland.
Distribution: The plant is widely distributed in the Northern
Hemisphere. With the exception of the most southerly parts of
Italy and the Iberian Peninsula it can be found all over Europe. Its
area of distribution extends through the Near East and the Caucasus to Western Mongolia. It also grows in Northern Asia and vast
areas of North America.
Parts used: Leaves (Folia Myrtilli); fruits (Fructus Myrtilli).
Harvesting time: Summer.
Harvesting instructions: Undamaged leaves were carefully dried,
so they did not turn brown. They are nearly odourless and have an
astringent taste.
The ripe fruits were dried in artificial heat. They have a weak
aroma and a sour-sweet slightly harsh taste.
Ingredients: The leaves of the bilberry contain arbutin, tannin,
flavonids, caffeine and chlorogen acid. The fruit contains 5−12
per cent tannin, approximately 30 per cent pectin, sugar, 1.5 per
cent arbutin, vitamin C and anthoycyan colouring.
Uses: The drug is prescribed as a diuretic and for rheumatic
complaints.
The tannins in the fruits are first released in the intestines, so they
do not damage the stomach and can act together with the pectin
against diarrhoea, bind poisons and in addition prevent their
reabsorption by means of their astringent qualities.
Side effects: The fruits are not poisonous. Hydrochinon poisoning
can follow extended use of the leaves.
History: The bilberry was first mentioned as a medicinal plant by
Abbess Hildegard of Bingen. The sixteenth century herbals, particularly that of Hieronymus Bock, give extensive details of the
plant's healing properties.

Bilberry

COWBERRY
Vaccinium vitis-idaea L.

Family: Ericaceae.

Description: The cowberry is a low shrublet up to 30 cm (1 ft) high with underground stolons covered in scaly leaves. From their aerial axillary buds develop round shoots which are covered in downy hair when young but later become bare. The alternate leaves are tough and leathery, dark green above and light green beneath and their slightly crenate margins are turned under. The white to reddish flowers are arranged in crowded clusters of several or many flowers. The open corolla is bell-shaped and pendulous and the style protrudes well forward. The berries at first white, later become scarlet-red and house many red-brown seeds.

Flowering time: Late spring to late summer.

Habitat: The cowberry forms an important undergrowth in pine-woods. It grows on humus-rich acid soil, poor in nutrients, on high and intermediate moorland and in the dwarf shrubby heathland of the higher mountains. It can withstand more drought and cold than the bilberry.

Distribution: The cowberry grows throughout the North Temperate Zone as far as the Cold Zone from Iceland and Great Britain across Scandinavia (beyond latitude 70°N) and Russia to Japan and right through North America. It can be found in the south as far as the Mediterranean, the Caucasus and the Himalayas.

Parts used: Leaves (Folia Vitis-idaei).

Harvesting time: Early autumn or fall.

Harvesting instructions: The leaves should, so far as possible, be plucked individually and dried at room temperature. Any brown discoloration can be ignored. The drug is odourless and has a harsh, slightly bitter taste.

Ingredients: Cowberries contain 4—6 per cent arbutin, tannin and flavonoids, such as hyperoside.

Uses: Cowberry leaves have, even in small quantities, the same effective ingredients as bearberry (Arctostaphylos) leaves. While it was previously used as an adulterant for this berry nowadays it is fully recognised as a substitute drug and used for gall-bladder complaints as a urine disinfectant. Because of its low arbutin content double the quantity can be used compared with Folia Uvae ursi. As its tannin content is also low, it is more agreeable too.

Side effects: Acute poisoning with the drug is not possible. But using large quantities of cowberry leaves over a long period can lead to chronic hydrochinon poisoning, causing anaemia, loss of strength and fatty degeneration of the liver.

History: Cowberry leaves have only recently been used medicinally.

Cowberry

VALERIAN   *Valeriana officinalis* L.

Family: Valerianaceae.

Description: This herbaceous plant, growing about 25–100 cm (10–39 in) high, survives from year to year by means of a short cylindrical rootstock with subterranean stolens. Apart from the number of basal leaves valerian produces an erect, grooved, slightly hairy stem in spring with opposite leaves which, like the basal leaves, are imparipinnate. At the end of the stem it bears an umbel-like multiple three-rayed inflorescence. When the fruit ripens the five small lobes of the calyx of the individual flowers change into a crown of projecting hairy pinnatisect rays (the pappus). The five fused petals are light pink to white. In a small recess above the base of the corolla tube the flowers secrete nectar, which attracts many insects, particularly flies.

Flowering time: Late spring to early autumn or fall.

Habitat: Valerian likes to colonise damp places in shady mountain ravines and riverside scrub, deciduous woods, damp meadows, ditches and the outskirts of woods, but also grows on sunny, rocky slopes up to 2000 m (6550 ft) or more.

Distribution: Valerian can be found over most of Europe apart from the extreme north and south. It can be found across the Caucasus, Siberia, Central Asia to Manchuria and Japan.

Parts used: Root (Radix Valerianae).

Harvesting time: Early to mid-autumn or fall.

Harvesting instructions: The roots were washed, split and dried in a stream of air at about 40°C. They assume a dark-green colour and as isovalerian acid splits off the typical valerian smell appears, which attracts cats. The drug first has a sweetish, but later a spicy and bitter taste.

Ingredients: The valerian roots contain, as a main ingredient, up to 5 per cent valepotriate, particularly valtrat, and approximately 1.5 per cent ethereal oil. Other constituents are mucilage and tannin.

Uses: The valepotriate and the ethereal oil have a calming and restraining effect, increase concentration and performance and have anti-convulsive characteristics. The drug was prescribed for states of excitement, insomnia, nervous heart complaints and anxiety states, as well as cramp in the gastro-intestinal tract, flatulence and colic.

Side effects: Regular use of large amounts of valerian causes headaches and heart disorders.

History: In searching for the effective principle of the drug, Thies discovered valepotriate (valeriana-epoxy-triester) in 1966, which proved effective in tests on animals and clinically and scientifically substantiated the use of valerian since antiquity. Up to 1950 the effect was generally attributed to the ethereal oil, though this was not confirmed pharmacologically.

Valerian

†WHITE HELLEBORE

Veratrum album L.

Family: Liliaceae.

Description: This perennial plant survives the winter by means of its tuberous taproot which produces false stems in spring before flowering. They are formed from long, tubular leaf sheaths fitted one inside another. They are downy felted underneath and smooth on top. Leaves with deep longitudinal folds form a basal rosette. The rhizome's terminal bud develops into a flower stem, densely hairy towards the top, reaching a maximum of 150 cm (5 ft) tall. The terminal inflorescence is a 30–60 cm (1–2 ft) long panicle formed of spike-shaped clusters of flowers and broad oval bracts. Each short-stemmed flower is borne in the axil of a small bract and is white to yellowish-green or green. The infertile shoots of the white hellebore differ mainly by their alternate leaves from the many species of gentian, whose leaves are invariably opposite.

Flowering time: Summer.

Habitat: The white hellebore is found particularly in mountain regions in damp meadows, mountain slopes fed by springs, resting places for cattle, flat moorland and light woody areas, generally in groups.

Distribution: The white hellebore colonises the South European mountains. Its northern limit in Central Europe runs through the South of France, the Swabian Mountains and the Sudeten Mountains.

Parts used: Rootstock (Rhizoma Veratri).

Harvesting time: Early to mid-autumn or fall.

Harvesting instructions: The rootstock is dug out and shaken free from earth, then washed thoroughly and dried in a well ventilated shady area. The drug is odourless and has a sharp and bitter taste. It causes sneezing when in powder form.

Beware! All parts of the plant are poisonous, particularly the taproot!

Ingredients: The taproot of the white false helleborine contains as the main ingredients veratrumalkaloids, which are amongst the most poisonous active elements in plants, also protoveratrin and germerin.

Uses: The drug was prescribed for high blood pressure because of its protoveratrin content but is no longer used for medicinal purposes. It was formerly used in cases of vomiting and diarrhoea, for fevers, rheumatism and neuralgia, and often externally against parasites, particularly in animal medicines, and as a sneezing powder.

Toxic effect: Poisoning leads to slowing of the pulse, vomiting, diarrhoea and cramp. Ingestion of only 1-2 gm of the drug results in death.

History: It is assumed this plant was used in antiquity and it certainly was used in the Middle Ages.

White Hellebore

WOOLLY MULLEIN   *Verbascum phlomoides* L.

Family: Scrophulariaceae.

Description: Woolly mullein is a biennial plant with a spindle-shaped branched taproot. It usually produces a rosette of large leaves in its first year, from the centre of which in the next year grows its upright, round stem up to 2 m (6½ ft) high, which, like the upper surface of the leaves, is densely felted with hair. The leaves are slightly notched, broadly elliptical on the lower part of the plant, narrowing down to a short stem on the ground, but in the middle and upper part of the plant cordate to ovate. The flowers are borne in axillary clusters of two to five, compact at first but later elongated. The 3−5 cm (1−2 in) wide fused, wheel-shaped corolla is brilliant yellow, the anthers reddish.

Every leaf of the large mullein (V. densiflorum BERTOL.), unlike those of the species described above, has a winged stem which runs down to the next leaf below. The small mullein (V. thapsus L.) usually has smaller flowers.

Flowering time: Mid-summer to early autumn or fall.

Habitat: Mulleins can be found in stony, sunny places and also on alluvial gravel. The large flowered Mullein is cultivated in small plots for drug extraction.

Distribution: Mulleins can be found all over Europe apart from the extreme northern areas.

Parts used: Flowers (Flores Verbasci).

Harvesting time: Mid to late summer.

Harvesting instructions: The drug Flores Verbasci consists of woolly mullein and great mullein flowers. The flowers without their calyces were harvested individually at midday in dry weather and dried as quickly as possible in a thin layer at about 40°C. They must not be allowed to turn brown during this process. The drug must be stored in airtight containers as it absorbs water. It must be checked frequently and if necessary driney-like smell and a sweet, slimy taste.

Ingredients: The flowers of the mullein contain approximately 3 per cent mucilage, saponins, flavonoids, hesperidin and verbascoside, and traces of ethereal oil, aucubin and yellow pigments.

Uses: The drug's mucilage content gives it an anti-irritant effect on the throat and its saponin content a discharging effect. It was used for catarrh in the upper respiratory tracts.

Side effects: The drug has no side effects.

History: The mullein root was often used in medicine in antiquity for diarrhoea, cramp, eye infections and healing wounds. Mullein has been known as a medicinal plant in Central Europe since the Middle Ages but the flowers have only recently been used.

Woolly Mullein

VERVAIN   *Verbena officinalis* L.

Family: Verbenaceae.

Description: This annual or perennial plant has a spindle-shaped, branched, white root. The lower part of its 30—80 cm (12—32 in) high stem is woody, the upper part partly branched and square in section. The opposite lateral branches are always shorter than the main stem. The leaves are opposite and roughly hairy, the lower ones relatively small with deep incisions, the middle ones larger and tripartite. The upper leaves are again smaller, while the uppermost have entire margins. The small flowers are grouped in many-flowered, glandular-hairy spikes at the apex of the plant and in the leaf axils continue to grow and form new flowers at the top while the lower ones are wilting. The lower part of the pinkish white to lilac corolla fuses into a bent tube. It has a five-part indistinctly two-lobed margin at the top.

Flowering time: Mid-summer to mid-autumn or fall.

Habitat: Vervain can be found scattered and in groups from the lowlands into the foothills of the mountains, in meadows, beside footpaths (particularly in villages), near fences and on walls and waste ground.

Distribution: The plant can be found from North Africa across Europe to Central and Northern Asia, and has been introduced to most other parts of the world. In Europe its northern limit runs from the British Isles across Denmark to Southern Sweden.

Parts used: Herbage (Herba Verbenae).

Harvesting time: Mid-summer to early autumn or fall.

Harvesting instructions: The upper parts of the plants were cut off with shears while in flower and spread out in a shaded and well ventilated place to dry. Only the upper part of the plant is harvested. The drug is almost odourless, and has a harsh, bitter taste.

Ingredients: The vervain contains glycoside verbenalin and hastatosid, furthermore, an alkaloid, tannin, bitter constituents and ethereal oil.

Uses: The drug is no longer used nowadays. It was previously employed in folk medicine as a bitter agent and also a diuretic.

Side effects: The glycosides are virtually non-poisonous. No side effects are known.

History: Several species of vervain were used as healing agents in antiquity by the Egyptians, Persians, Greeks and Romans. These plants were also known to the Germanic and Celtic peoples. In antiquity they were used almost exclusively for healing wounds, but in the Middle Ages vervain was used for many illnesses.

Vervain

COMMON SPEEDWELL   *Veronica officinalis* L.

Family: Scrophulariaceae.
Description: The common speedwell overwinters by means of its creeping rootstock that produces 10 to 20 cm (4−8 in) long prostrate shoots in spring, bearing ascending side shoots and erect inflorescences. The opposite leaves, like the rest of the plant, are covered in stiff hairs. The flowers are arranged in a very short stemmed clustered inflorescence which develops from the axil of one of the leaves and continues to grow slightly after flowering. The individual flowers sit in the axils of small bracts on short upright stems. The light violet, four-tipped corolla consists of five fused petals that form a very short tube at the base. Common speedwell can easily be differentiated from other species of speedwell by its greater hairiness, the leaf axillary position of its inflorescence, its short pedicels and four-leaved calyx, but above all by the light violet colour of its flowers.
Flowering time: Summer.
Habitat: Common speedwell can be found from the lowlands into the Alps in woods and on heathland.
Distribution: This plant grows over Europe and the Middle East and is also a native plant of North America.
Parts used: Flowering herbage (Herba Veronicae).
Harvesting time: Summer.
Harvesting instructions: The aerial parts of the plant are gathered and dried, during which they should not be turned. Their colour should not alter. The drug has a weak smell and a harsh bitter taste.
Ingredients: The herbage of the common speedwell contains the glycoside aucubin, bitter ingredients, tannin and traces of ethereal oil.
Uses: The drug is no longer used, but once served in folk medicine as a discharging agent for respiratory diseases. From time to time it was used for diarrhoea, gout and rheumatism.
Side effects: No side effects have emerged when using the drug. But its aucubin content can poison cattle.
History: Speedwell was not mentioned in the writings of antiquity, as it is rare in the Mediterranean countries. A detailed description of the plant appeared in the herbal written by Hieronymus Bock, one of the best botanists of the Middle Ages. He lists all complaints for which the speedwell had been prescribed. Its importance as a medicinal plant is illustrated by the fact that in 1690 Johannes Francus published a book in which he dealt exclusively with the speedwell. The plant's importance later diminished greatly.

Common Speedwell

SWEET VIOLET   *Viola odorata* L.

Family: Violaceae.
Description: This plant generally produces stolons up to 20 cm
(8 in) long and survives the winter by means of a short, thick,
often aerial rootstock. Early in spring a leaf rosette develops at its
apex. The flowers grow from the axils of the basal leaves as there
is no main stem. The 3−7 cm (1−3 in) long pedicel bears two tiny
leaves (bracteoles) at, or just above the middle. The five petals
are deep violet, but white at the base. The spurs of the lower
petals reach beyond the sepals' appendices. Into them protrude
the extensions of the very short feathered stamens, each of which
has a yolk-yellow excrescence at the tip. These secrete nectar in
the spur. The flower has a lovely fragrance.
Flowering time: Early to mid-spring.
Habitat: The sweet violet is found in large numbers in moist
places, in hedges, light woodland, beside streams, round the
outskirts of woods and, of course, in gardens.
Distribution: The sweet violet can be found all over Central
Europe but probably originates in the Upper Rhine plain. It also
grows in the Caucasus, Turkey and the Mediterranean area, as
well as Atlantic Europe. It has been introduced into scattered
areas of North America.
Parts used: Rootstock (Rhizoma Violae).
Harvesting time: Early to mid-autumn or fall.
Harvesting instructions: The rootstock is dug out, shaken free of
earth, then washed and dried in the air. The drug is almost
odourless and has a sharp burning taste.
Ingredients: The sweet violet contains the effective ingredient
saponin, furthermore bitter constituents, approximately 0.4 per
cent ethereal oil with methysalicylat and the alkaloid odoratin.
The previously listed ingredient of violin (Violet Emetin) in the
drug could not be confirmed. It is assumed to be a mixture of
saponins with an alkaloid.
Uses: The drug has an effect similar to the South American ipecac
(Radix Ipecacuanhae), because of its saponines. Although it no
longer has a role to play as an emetic, due to the discharging effect
of the saponines, it is used as a substitute drug of equal value for
ipecac. The sweet violet root is not identical with the so-called
violet root or orris root, which is the rhizome of various iris species
(Rhizoma Iridis).
Side effects: The drug has an emetic effect.
History: In the medicine of antiquity the sweet violet was in
constant use as a medicine from Hippocrates onwards. It was of
no less importance in the Middle Ages, as Hieronymus Bock
reported, discussing the plant's medicinal applications at great
length. Sebastian Kneipp also used the violet root quite frequently.

Sweet Violet

HEARTEASE

Viola tricolor L.

Family: Violaceae.

Description: Heartease is usually a perennial plant. The yellow-ish-green, 10—20 cm (4—8 in) long shoots have squarish stems and rise from the ground. The alternate leaves are set fairly close together at the base of the stem but further apart towards the top. The pedicels arise singly in the axils of the leaves. Each bears two small bracts towards the top and a single 1 to 3 cm (1 in) diameter flower at the end. The petals usually vary in colour, from light yellow, whitish and pink to violet. The two side petals are bent outwards and have a white to yellowish brush-appendage. The front petal has a distinct spur. The fruit is a three-lobed capsule, which opens to expel a roughly 1 mm diameter seed with a small seed callus (Elaiosom) attached. Ants like to eat these, which takes care of the plant's distribution.

Flowering time: Late spring to mid-autumn or fall.

Habitat: Heartease is often found in fields, mountain meadows, and on sandy soil from the lowlands to mountainous areas over 2000 m (6560 ft) above sea level.

Distribution: This plant can be found all over Europe from the far North to the Mediterranean. It is found in the east to the Altai and Western India.

Parts used: Herbage (Herba Violae tricoloris).

Harvesting time: Late spring to mid-summer.

Harvesting instructions: The aerial parts of the plant are harvested while in flower and carefully dried in the air. The drug is almost odourless and has a slight, sweet, slimy taste.

Ingredients: The herbage of the heartease contains as the main ingredients, saponins and flavonoid glycosides. Other constituents of the drug are tannin, mucilage, and traces of ethereal oil with salicylic acid methylester.

Uses: The drug is used primarily for its saponine content. It is therefore usually prescribed as a discharging agent for complaints of the respiratory tract. Its diuretic and sudorific effects are probably due to the flavonoides. This drug was also used for certain skin complaints.

Side effects: If taken in large doses or over an extended period, the drug can produce sickness and vomiting.

History: The drug was known in antiquity but not used. The sixteenth century herbals recommended it for skin complaints.

Heartease

MISTLETOE
Viscum album L.

Family: Loranthaceae.

Description: Mistletoe is an evergreen shrub parasitic on trees, usually a globular bushy plant up to a metre (3 ft) in diameter. The shrub sends its vertical roots into the bark and wood of its host plant by dissolving their cells and withdraws the resulting water and nutrients which it processes itself by means of its evergreen leaves (i.e. it is a semi-parasite). The short thick stem bears greenish brown segmented branches which bear inconspicuous flowers at the end of each forked shoot between the forked branches. These are normally dioecious male and female flowers rarely appearing on the same bush. They are borne in clusters of three or five in the axils of small bracts. Each berry-like fruit, green at first, later white to yellowish, and up to pea size, contains one or occasionally two seeds surrounded by slimy flesh. The berries ripen in November or December of the following year and are distributed by birds. The deciduous tree mistletoe is distinct from the coniferous tree mistletoe of firs and pines (V. laxum).

Flowering time: Deciduous tree mistletoe, late winter to mid-spring, coniferous tree mistletoe, Spring.

Habitat: The shrub is a parasite of various trees and grows from the lowlands to mountains of medium height.

Distribution: The deciduous tree mistletoe can be found eastwards to Western Iran and Northern Asia, the coniferous tree mistletoe mostly in Southern and Central Europe.

Parts used: Whole herbage (Herba Visci albi).

Harvesting time: Early to mid-spring and early to mid-autumn or fall.

Harvesting instructions: The mistletoe bushes are knocked off the trees with a pole or cut off with secateurs after climbing the tree. The useful parts are threaded on a line to dry in a heated room. The drug has a weak rancid smell and a bitter taste.

Ingredients: It contains viscotoxin and other polypeptides, acetylcholin, cholin, histamine, gama-amino butter acid and oleanol acid.

Uses: The effectiveness of mistletoe preparations for arteriosclerosis and high blood pressure is debatable. The constituents acetylcholin and viscotoxin are effective when given as intravenous injections but when taken orally are destroyed in the gastro-intestinal tract. Possibly the gamma-amino butter acid plays a part in its effectiveness. The polypeptides extracted from the drug are nowadays used experimentally in tumour therapy.

Side effects: There is no poisoning when the drug is taken orally, but viscotoxin is a strong heart poison.

History: Mistletoe was always considered as a holy plant. The medicinal draught prepared from the mistletoe was hailed as a universal remedy. The herbals of the sixteenth century recommended it for epilepsy and cramp.

Mistletoe

BRIEF BIOGRAPHIES

Avicenna (Ibn Sina) (980-1037). Born in Bokhara, died in Hamadam. One of the greatest of the Arabian doctors. His *Canon* exercised a decisive influence on the further development of medicine for centuries. This work contains the collected wisdom of the medicine of antiquity.

Bock, Hieronymus (1498-1554). Born in Heidersbach near Heidelberg, died as a doctor in Hornbach. Bock is one of the earliest German plant researchers. In 1546 he published his *New Kreutterbuch (New Herbal)*, containing many illustrations, in which he attempted to produce a clearly arranged classification of plants.

Boerhaave, Hermann (1668-1738). Held the Chair of Theoretical Medicine at the University of Leyden (Holland), and considered the best doctor in Europe. Boerhaave taught Albrecht von Haller and Gerhard van Swieten.

Charlemagne (Karl der Grosse) (742-814). Frankish king and Holy Roman Emperor. He gave exact instructions for the cultivation of healing plants in his *Capitulare*.

Dioscorides, Pedanios. This Greek doctor lived in the first century AD and wrote the *Great Pharmacology*, which comprised information on all the healing plants used in antiquity and their uses. Almost all the herbals that appeared in the Middle Ages were based upon Dioscorides' book.

Fuchs, Leonhart (1501-1566). Doctor and plant researcher who produced splendid descriptions and illustrations of plants, revised the writings of Hippocrates and Galen, and turned against Avicenna. Fuchs was also known as an opponent of Vesalius' system of anatomy. The fuchsia was later named in Fuchs' honour.

Galen (Claudius Galenos) (131-200). Born in Pergamum, died in Rome. One of the most important doctors of antiquity, whose teachings on the healing art were a major influence for 1500 years. He described drugs according to their uses and powers. The Galenic remedies still used today are pharmaceutical preparations from drugs in their natural state, as against isolated or synthesised substances or raw drugs.

Hildegard of Bingen (1098-1179). Born in Bockelheim near Kreuznach, died as Abbess of the Rupertsberg near Bingen and later canonised. She produced two medical books among other writings, based on the medicine of antiquity.

Hippocrates (circa 460-377 BC). The most important doctor of antiquity, who lived on the island of Kos and received the name 'Father of Medicine'. He was the first to put medicine on a scientific basis. His disciples were known as the Hippocratic school.

Kneipp, Sebastian (1821-1897). Priest and exponent of natural healing, who served in Worishofen from 1855 and founded an establishment there for water treatment.

Linnaeus (Carl von Linne) (1707-1778). Born at Rashult in Smaland, Sweden, died in Uppsala. Published his *Systema Naturae* in 1735 in which he classified plants in general and species according to their sexual characteristics. He benefited from the earlier work of John Ray in England, but is credited with the binomial system in which each plant or animal is given a generic and a specific name. He it was who named Man *Homo sapiens*.

Paracelsus (Theophrastus Bombastus von Hohenheim) (1493-1541). Doctor and philosopher, born in Einsiedeln, Switzerland, died in Salzburg, Austria. Paracelsus was sharply critical of medieval medicine and was a reformer of medical practice. He took his medicines from nature. Healing plants held an important place in Paracelsus' teachings, as also in his doctrine of signatures, which proved untenable however. This claimed that for every kind of sickness there existed some plant which could be used effectively against it and which could be recognised by its similarity to the symptoms of the illness.

Pliny (Gaius P. Secundus Plinius) (23-79). Roman writer, who entered life at the time of Vesuvius' eruption. He wrote a several volume *Natural History* which summarised the knowledge of natural science in his day. He also worked with the medicinal plants used by the common people, in part very superficially, which led to the use of strange flowers in the superstitious medical practices of the Middle Ages.

Rhazes (850-923). Lived at Rai in Khorazan. Considered to be the greatest physician of Islam.

Theophrastus (circa 377-287 BC). Born on the island of Lesbos, died in Athens. Greek philosopher, teacher of Plato and Aristotle, who wrote a *Plant History*, from which he became known as the 'Father of Ancient Botany'.

Valerius Cordus (1515-1544). Born in Erfurt, died in Rome. He undertook many journeys on which he studied plants, visiting Switzerland, Italy and Scandinavia. He lectured about Dioscorides at the University of Wittenberg in 1540. Cordus produced the first official German medical book in 1535.

GLOSSARY OF BOTANICAL TERMS

achene a one-seeded ovary, normally separate from its fellows

actinomorphic radially symmetrical

adventitious of a plant occurring in places outside its normal range and habitats

annual a plant which germinates, flowers, seeds and dies within a year

anther the part of the stamen containing the pollen grains

apomixis the production of viable seed without fertilisation

appressed (also **adpressed**) pressed flat against a surface; usually referring to hairs

auricle a lobe at the base of a leaf (rarely a petal) which is often ear-like in shape and typically clasps the stem

awn a long stiff bristle-like projection at the end or side of an organ

axil the angle between a leaf or shoot and a main stem; hence, an axillary growth, flower or bud

berry a fleshy fruit, typically rounded and containing several hard seeds; often loosely used (e.g. strawberry, blackberry)

biennial a plant which germinates and develops in the first year and flowers, seeds and dies in the second, though sometimes capable of behaving like an annual

blade the flattened part of a leaf or petal

bract a leaf-like or scale-like organ, usually smaller than the true leaves of the plant, and in the axils of which flower stems often develop

bulb an underground storage organ, consisting of separate, fleshy scales

bulbil a miniature bulb arising among the flowers (as in *Allium*), or in the leaf axils (as in *Lilium croceum*), from which new plants can arise

calyx a collective term for the sepals of a flower

capsule a dry fruit of at least two carpels, splitting open when ripe

carpel one female, seed-bearing unit of a flower

cartilaginous hard, tough tissue, often not green

catkin a tight, usually hanging spike of small flowers

ciliate edged with hairs

claw the narrow basal part of some petals, often hidden inside the calyx

cleistogamic referring to flowers which never open normally and are self-pollinated (as ocurring in *Viola, Oxalis*)

cone the fruit of some trees of the Conifer tribe, consisting of stiff, hard scales sheltering the seeds; also used here of the cone-shaped spore-bearing organs of some Club-mosses and Selaginellas

corm a swollen underground stem, not composed of scales like a bulb, usually in a tunic; next year's corm is almost always formed on top of the old one

corolla a collective term for the petals of a flower

cyme a flower-head in which the growing point is always terminated by a flower, and fresh flowers occur on new side growing points. Such clusters are usually reversed-cone-shaped, with the oldest flowers at the top and centre

deciduous losing leaves in winter

decussate of leaves in opposed pairs with each pair at right angles to the next

dehisce of seed vessels, to open or split to release the seeds

disk floret the tubular florets (as opposed to the ray florets) which occupy part of or sometimes all the flower-heads of some Compositae

drupe a usually fleshy fruit with one or more seeds each in a hard 'stone'

epicalyx a calyx-like structure immediately outside the true calyx

escaped of a cultivated plant found outside gardens, but not properly naturalised

evergreen not losing all leaves in winter

fall the outer set of petals in Irises, usually larger than the inner and typically out-spread or drooping petals

family a classificatory term for a group of plants sharing many common characters of the flower (not normally of foliage, habit, etc.)

ferny a word used loosely to indicate which leaves are long and narrow and divided into many fine, more or less parallel segments as in many Ferns

filament the stalk of the stamen, which bears the anthers

floret a small flower, especially when one of a dense cluster

follicle a dry fruit of one carpel, often swollen and elongated, opening along one side

form (Latin **forma**) a slight but distinguishable variant within a species

genus (plural **genera**) a classificatory term for the main subsections of a family, each genus being composed, usually, of several species

gland a small organ usually containing an oil or resin, which may be in or on the surface, or on a stalk when it is called a glandular hair; often making the plant aromatic or sticky

glaucous bluish or greyish

head a loose term for a dense group of flowers or fruits at the end of one stalk

hep the fruit of a rose; also spelt **hip**

herbaceous of a plant, non-woody, the upper growth usually dying back to ground level in winter; of a plant organ, having the texture and colour of leaves

hood a loose term for the hood- or helmet-shape created by the upper sepal, or three upper sepals together, in orchids, or by the upper petal as in *Pedicularis*

inflorescence a complete flower-head excluding the topmost stem-leaf, including all flowers, stalks and bracts

introduced of an alien plant, introduced deliberately or accidentally into the wild and now fully naturalised as if native

involucre an often calyx-like structure formed by leaf-like bracts surrounding a dense flower-head, as typically in Composites

keel a sharp central edge on an organ; also the combined lower petals of flowers of the Pea family

lanceolate, lance-shaped shaped like a lance-head — much longer than wide, with broad base, narrowing to the tip

lemma the lower of the two flower-bracts in grasses

ligule a small projection where a leaf-blade and its sheath meet, as typically in grasses; also, the strap-shaped extension of the ray floret in Composites

limb the flattened, spreading part of a calyx or corolla which is tubular at the base

linear long and narrow, with sides more or less parallel

lip one perianth segment, or a group of combined ones, forming a flap-like projection distinct from the rest

membranous dry, thin and flexible, not green

midrib the central vein of a leaf

monocarpic flowering and seeding once only, and then dying, usually after more than two years (the term usually excludes annuals and biennials with a specific life)

naturalised of an alien plant which has established itself as if native in the wild

nectary a gland giving off a sugary liquid, usually in the flower to attract insects

node a stem division; a point where a leaf or branch grows from the stem, especially if swollen

nut a one-seeded fruit with a hard outer shell

nutlet a small nut-like seed

ob- as a prefix, inverted, or with the widest part above the middle

ovary the part of the flower enclosing the ovules

ovate with an egg-shaped outline, the broadest part at the base

ovule the structure containing the female germ-cell which after fertilisation becomes the seed

palea the upper of the two flower-bracts in grasses

panicle a branched, usually conical, cluster of stalked flowers, the youngest of which are at the top

papillae small projections

pappus hairs or bristles which replace the calyx in Composites, and are often retained at the top of the seed

parasite a plant deriving nourishment from other living plants to which it attaches itself; complete parasites have no green leaves

perennial living for more than two years and normally flowering every year

perianth all the floral 'leaves', including both sepals and petals

perianth segment one floral 'leaf', used especially when petals and sepals are indistinguishable, as in the Lily family

petal one of the inner floral 'leaves', usually showy and coloured, which together form the corolla

petaloid petal-like; as a noun, a petal-like organ intermediate between petals and stamens

pinnatifid of leaves cut into lobes in two rows, not as far as the midrib

pinnatisect of leaves cut into lobes in two rows, mostly to the midrib

plica a tooth or small lobe between the main corolla lobes of Gentians

pod a general term for any more or less swollen, dry, splitting fruit of one carpel (section)

pollinium the structure formed by massed pollen-grains in Orchids

pore a small opening, typically in a seed pod

procumbent straggling loosely over the surface of the ground

prostrate lying more or less close to the surface of the ground

race (geographical) a localised group of plants differing from other localised groups in minor characters

raceme an unbranched, usually conical, cluster of stalked flowers, the youngest of which are at the top

ray one of the stalks of an umbel

ray floret a floret, tubular at the base, one side of which is elongated into a strap-shape, in the flower-heads of many Composites

receptacle the often thickened upper part of the stem which carries the flower parts, or the florets in Composites

rhizome a more or less permanent thickened underground stem

rhombic roughly diamond-shaped

rosette a cluster of leaves, typically at ground level, radiating from a central point

runner a creeping permanent overground stem which roots and forms new plants at its end or nodes

saprophyte a plant living on dead or decaying organic matter; complete saprophytes have no green leaves

scorpioid cyme a curving, one-sided spike-like cluster, with the youngest flower at the apex, as in Forget-me-not

sepal one of the outer floral 'leaves', together forming the calyx; usually green but sometimes showy and petal-like, especially if replacing the petals as in *Anemone* or *Clematis*

sessile stalkless

shrub a woody, branching plant with no main trunk

silicula a pod-like fruit of the Crucifer family, often broader than long and never more than twice as long as broad

siliqua a pod-like fruit of the Crucifer family, at least twice as long as broad, usually much more

sinus the cleft between two lobes

sorus (plural **sori**) a group of sporangia in ferns

species (abbreviated sp., pluarl spp.) a classification term for a group of individual plants, distinct but having similar characters, which will interbreed, and together form a genus

spike a dense, elongated flower-head of stalkless or short-stalked flowers; often used loosely as of narrow elongated panicles; also of the narrow or cone-like spore-bearing heads of some Horsetails and Ferns

sporangia spore-bearing structures

sporophyll leaves which carry sporangia in Club-mosses

spur a usually hollow, tubular to sac-shaped extension of a petal or sepal, which often contains nectar

stamen the male reproductive organ of a flower, consisting of pollen-bearing anthers and, usually, a filament (stalk)

staminode a sterile or rudimentary stamen with no pollen, sometimes developed in a different way, e.g. as a nectary

standard the broad upper petal of the flower in the Pea family; one of the inner, usually upright perianth segments of an Iris

starry of hairs, branching in a star-shape

stigma the pollen-receptive part of the female reproductive organs of a flower: usually on top of the style, and typically sticky

stipule a scale-like or leaf-like appendage at the base of a leaf-stalk

stolon a creeping stem which roots and produces new plants at the nodes, and eventually decays

style the more or less elongated, stalk-like projection of the ovary, bearing the stigma

subshrub a plant with woody base and herbaceous upper part, like Lavender

subspecies (abbreviated ssp., plural sspp.) a group of plants within a species, with several distinctive characters; often a geographical race

truncate having a square or broad, straight end

tube the fused part of a calyx or corolla

tuber an underground swollen stem which is a storage organ, and is neither a bulb nor a corm

tunic a dry, brownish, usually papery covering around a bulb or corm

umbel a cluster of stalks arising at the same point from the top of a stem

valve one of the segments into which a seed capsule splits

variety (abbreviated var.) a group of plants within a species with at least one distinctive character such as unusual flower colour

vein strands of conducting and strengthening tissue in a leaf or petal, usually clearly visible

viviparous of a plant, bearing miniature plants, bulbs or offsets which sprout while still on the parent

whorl several organs arising at the same level

wing a thin,projecting extension of an organ such as a pod, calyx or stem; also the side petals of the flowers of the Pea family

zygomorphic of flowers, symmetrical in the vertical plane only, thus divisible into two halves lengthwise

INDEX OF COMMON NAMES

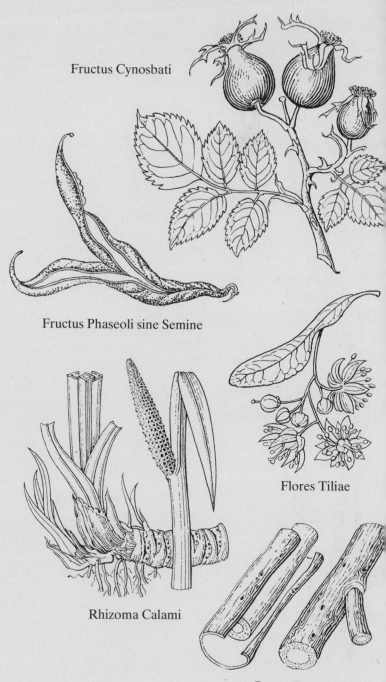

Fructus Cynosbati

Fructus Phaseoli sine Semine

Rhizoma Calami

Flores Tiliae

Cortex Frangulae